The World's Landscapes
edited by J. M. Houston

New Zealand

The World's Landscapes
edited by J. M. Houston

China Yi-Fu Tuan
The Soviet Union W. H. Parker
Ireland A. R. Orme
New Zealand K. B. Cumberland & J. S. Whitelaw

The World's Landscapes

New Zealand

Kenneth B. Cumberland

Professor and Head of the Department of Geography,
The University of Auckland, New Zealand

and

James S. Whitelaw

Lecturer in the Department of Geography,
Monash University, Australia

ALDINE PUBLISHING COMPANY
CHICAGO

First published 1970 by
ALDINE PUBLISHING COMPANY
529 South Wabash Avenue
Chicago, Illinois 60605

and

Longman Group Limited
London

SBN 202–10039 (clothbound edition), 202–10040 (paperbound edition)

Library of Congress Catalog
Card Number 73–110624

PRINTED IN THE UNITED STATES OF AMERICA

Editor's Preface

Despite the multitude of geographical books that deal with differing areas of the world, no series has before attempted to explain man's role in moulding and changing its diverse landscapes. At the most there are books that study individual areas in detail, but usually in language too technical for the general reader. It is the purpose of this series to take regional geographical studies to the frontiers of contemporary research on the making of the world's landscapes. This is being done by specialists, each in his own area, yet in non-technical language that should appeal to both the general reader and to the discerning student.

We are leaving behind us an age that has viewed Nature as an objective reality. Today we are living in a more pragmatic, less idealistic age. The nouns of previous thought forms are the verbs of a new outlook. Pure thought is being replaced by the use of knowledge for a technological society, busily engaged in changing the face of the earth. It is an age of operational thinking. The very functions of Nature are being threatened by scientific takeovers, and it is not too fanciful to predict that the daily weather, the biological cycles of life processes, as well as the energy of the atom will become harnessed to human corporations. Thus it becomes imperative that all thoughtful citizens of our world today should know something of the changes man has already wrought in his physical habitat, and which he is now modifying with accelerating power.

Studies of man's impact on the landscapes of the earth are expanding rapidly. They involve diverse disciplines such as Quaternary sciences, archaeology, history and anthropology, with subjects that range from pollen analysis, to plant domestication, field systems, settlement patterns and industrial land use. But with his sense of place, and his sympathy for synthesis, the geographer is well placed to handle this diversity of data in a meaningful manner. The appraisal of landscape changes, how and when man has altered and remoulded the surface of the earth, is both pragmatic and interesting to a wide range of readers.

The concept of 'landscape' is of course both concrete and elusive. In its Anglo-Saxon origin, *landskift* referred to some unit of area that was a natural entity, such as the lands of a tribe or of a feudal lord. It was only at the end of the sixteenth century that through the influence of Dutch landscape painters, the word also acquired the idea of a unit of visual perceptions, of a view. In the German *Landschaft*, both definitions have been maintained, a source of confusion and uncertainty in the use of the term. However, despite scholarly analysis of its ambiguity, the concept of landscape has increasing currency precisely because of its ambiguity. It refers to the total man-land complex in place and time, suggesting spatial interactions, and indicative of visual features that we can select, such as field and settlement patterns, set in the mosaics of

v

relief, soils and vegetation. Thus the 'landscape' is the point of reference in the selection of widely ranging data. It is the tangible context of man's association with the earth. It is the documentary evidence of the power of human perception to mould the resources of nature into human usage, a perception as varied as his cultures. Today, the ideological attitudes of man are being more dramatically imprinted on the earth than ever before, owing to technological capabilities.

This book should command a wide interest. For there can be fewer areas of the world that have witnessed such violent and dramatic changes of landscape, as that imposed by the European settlers on New Zealand in the last 125 years. And yet, even here, the earlier Polynesian migrants had already induced the supposedly indigenous grasslands of South Island and had disturbed the forest cover of North Island in their relatively brief history of less than a millennium. In this fascinating description the two authors, who are well known authorities of their subject, outline the historic and regional changes imposed by the moahunters, the Maoris, and the Europeans, in a small area with a remarkable variety of terrain, climate and organic life. It is hoped that in addition to its interest to students of the subject, this book will arouse the general concern of all New Zealanders, towards the safeguard of their scenic heritage for tomorrow.

J. M. Houston

Contents

List of Illustrations

(Italic type denotes a map)

Acknowledgements

We are grateful to the following for permission to reproduce photographs:—
V. C. Browne: Figs. 8, 19, 22, 29; '*N.Z. Farmer*': Fig. 16; N.Z. Forest Service,
photos by J. A. Johns: Figs. 3, 4, 10; *N.Z. Herald and Weekly News*: Figs. 2,
18, 20, 23: N.Z. National Publicity Studios: Figs. 6, 7, 9, 11, 14, 28; N.Z. Soil
Conservation and Rivers Control Council: Fig. 25; Whites Aviation Ltd.:
Figs. 13 and 31.

Author's Note

Chapters 1, 2, 3 and 4 were written by Dr. Whitelaw and are partly based on
the previous publications of Professor Cumberland. Dr. Whitelaw also wrote
Chapters 9 and 10. Professor Cumberland is the author of Chapters 6, 7, 8
and 11.
The authors are grateful for the assistance of Mr. D. Branch, who drew the
maps, and Mrs. M. Sexton and Miss M. Fisher, who typed the manuscript.

Introduction

In a technological age of jet transport, space travel, massive hydroelectric dams and atomic energy installations, it is easy to discern and appreciate the role that man has played in moulding the landscapes of the world. The agency of man on earth is apparent in landscapes which are shaped overnight by the construction of motorways, or patterned, painted and repaired by contoured strip cropping and other farm conservation techniques, or cluttered and made chaotic within a few years by housing, factories and fields in jumbled and unplanned disarray on the outer suburban fringe of mushrooming cities, or disfigured by the ugly, raw wounds of eroding topsoils and devastated vegetation. It is less obvious in regions occupied for centuries by patient, toiling peasant communities where the pattern of life and the rural scene are regulated by the seasons and often imperceptibly different from what they were generations ago, and where western technology has made as yet little impression. Man, however, is today in the process of committing the landscapes of the world to an increasing momentum of change. None are now too remote: none free from the impact or the threat of twentieth-century man's expanding economy and input of energy.

The more we become aware of the extent of man's ecological dominance and of his role in changing the face of the earth, and of the way in which he does it – whether it be deliberate, purposeful and obvious, or accidental, insidious and long unsuspected – the clearer becomes the fact that this process is ancient and reaches back not only much further in human time than we had imagined but to the very day man first kindled a fire and made a primitive tool. Wherever and whenever men have lived they have had a role in altering the aspect of the earth – a role that has constantly enlarged and become more potent with the duration of human occupation, with growth in numbers and with elaboration of skills.

In many parts of the world – and certainly in much of Africa, Asia and Europe – man has been evaluating the potential of his habitat in terms of the skills available to him, organizing his life in relation to its resources, and transforming the face of the land for hundreds of thousands of years, slowly and subtly at first but with increasing power and effect. The disturbance and modification of the organic world has for the most part been a gradual though persistent process, subject to the vagaries of climate, the prevailingly snail-paced natural changes in the habitat and the disturbing influence of the local migratory comings and goings and contact and conflict of human communities with but relatively minor differences in skills and technology.

In other parts of the world – in the Americas and Australia for example – similar slow and steady changes in vegetation, animal life, terrain and waters of the land were worked by men of limited technology and small numbers until, abruptly, land and landscapes were subject to the incursion from a great distance of men of alien, strikingly different and much more advanced skills and technology. The gradual transformation of the face of the land was displaced by the working of profound changes as cataclysmic in their speed and effect both on the face of the land and the life of its indigenous people as the most violent of natural changes and calamities that had occurred since 'hominization'.

New Zealand falls into this category. But there can be few parts of the world where the human transformation of the aspect of the land has been compressed into so short a period, where the processes are so recent, the effects so apparent and where the careful scientific study of processes and effects, even the earliest of them, is likely to be so rewarding. There may be other frontiers of human settlement to which man came later; there are other territories to which the impact of western technology was carried more recently. But there can be no other isolated, insular land area, more than 100,000 square miles in extent, embracing such variety of terrain, climate and organic life, in which the total extent of human occupance is compressed into so short a time, the impact of Europe so sharply defined and the outcome of the agency of man so clearly depicted in the landscape.

None can say with precision when man first struggled ashore in these remote Pacific islands. Available evidence suggests it was little more than a thousand years ago, but it may yet prove to have been before the birth of Christ. However, until A.D. 1350 not more than 15,000 to 25,000 Polynesians are ever likely to have lived in New Zealand at one time. About then another of the minor migratory waves of humankind across the water expanse of the Pacific touched New Zealand shores and brought not only added numbers but a somewhat more elaborate range of Eastern Polynesian skills. Current anthropological and archaeological thought suggests that both the earlier and later Polynesian peoples and cultures to be established in Aotearoa overlapped in time and place, the technology of the later immigrants proving gradually superior.

Abel Janszoon Tasman was the harbinger of western civilization in New Zealand. As far as we know James Cook – 127 years later and exactly 200 years ago – was apparently the first European to have contact with land and people and to leave behind evidence of that contact. At that time the Polynesians in New Zealand may have numbered more than 250,000. European residence followed, both temporary and permanent; and it occurred at first on remote and scattered portions of the coastline. Organized colonial settlement by Europeans did not get under way until 1840. It was not until 1909 that the number of people in New Zealand reached a million – one person to every 66 acres or ten per square mile. In 1952 the population attained 2 million. In 1969 the number was 2,780,000.

The role of the moahunter and of his Maori successor in disturbing and displacing elements of the organic world in these uniquely 'temperate' and southerly Polynesian islands is not always clear. For long they were held up as paragons of conservation and as examples of how man could live in harmony with Nature without disrupting it. Archaeological, pedological, botanical and zoological evidence now suggests that in relation to their limited numbers, the level of their neolithic technology and the relative shortness of their uninterrupted occupance of the land, they worked profound and lasting changes. They may have transformed the vegetation of large areas, brought extinction to up to forty species of birds, created manmade soil profiles, and sculptured hills, promontories and offshore islands as effectively to their particular requirements as if they had had bulldozers on hand.

But whatever part the Polynesian played in modifying the pristine landscape in upwards of 1,000 years, it is nothing compared with the wholesale and ruthlessly effective transformation accomplished by the European – with the help of his Polynesian contemporaries – in the brief century that has elapsed since the 1860s by when he had managed to establish a foothold in 'six colonies' on the coasts of the North and South Islands.

In what follows an attempt has been made to describe briefly the pre-human landscape in so far as it is now possible to reconstruct it, to isolate and distinguish the role of Polynesian man in moulding the landscape before 1840, to outline the rude and ruthless progress of European settlement and technology in the century that followed and, by taking examples of the immense diversity of sharply contrasted manmade, man-modified and still predominantly wild landscapes, to illustrate the character of the contemporary New Zealand scene. We begin before the beginning of this strange and enthralling human adventure – before the first man made a silent landfall, probably famished and near death, on an alien, remote, southern shore in the vastness of the southwest Pacific.

Part One
The original scene

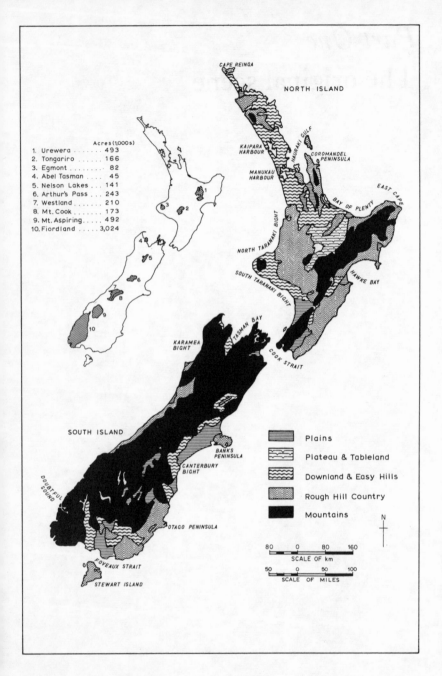

Acres (1000s)
1. Urewera 493
2. Tongariro 166
3. Egmont 82
4. Abel Tasman 45
5. Nelson Lakes ... 141
6. Arthur's Pass .. 243
7. Westland 210
8. Mt. Cook 173
9. Mt. Aspiring.... 492
10. Fiordland 3,024

CAPE REINGA

NORTH ISLAND

KAIPARA HARBOUR

HAURAKI GULF

COROMANDEL PENINSULA

MANUKAU HARBOUR

EAST CAPE

BAY OF PLENTY

NORTH TARANAKI BIGHT

SOUTH TARANAKI BIGHT

HAWKE BAY

KARAMEA BIGHT

TASMAN BAY

COOK STRAIT

SOUTH ISLAND

BANKS PENINSULA

CANTERBURY BIGHT

DOUBTFUL SOUND

OTAGO PENINSULA

FOVEAUX STRAIT

STEWART ISLAND

Plains

Plateau & Tableland

Downland & Easy Hills

Rough Hill Country

Mountains

N

80   0   80   160
SCALE OF km

50   0   50   100
SCALE OF MILES

1. *Physical landscapes and* (inset) *national parks*

Chapter 1
The pre-human landscape

What was New Zealand like before man first set foot in the country? Were there any major differences in the landscape before man arrived to attack the virgin bush, to alter the soil forming processes, to hunt and gather the bird, fish and plant life? Can a reconstruction of the pre-human landscape be made from which to measure and note and appreciate the succeeding changes and modifications effected by man? As an approximate base from which to work the year A.D. 500 has been taken as an appropriate time at which to attempt answers to such questions.

New Zealand was a land of extremes. In some ways the landscapes of both North and South Islands were much more similar in pre-human times than they are now. Forest mantled and smoothed the outline of both islands. In the North Island the vigorous vegetation cover extended from subtropic strand to mountain top while in the South Island it clothed and masked the country from golden sandspit, across gravel and loess plain, downland and basin to the treeline. But the virgin territory of New Zealand also presented a remarkable number of contrasts in natural landscapes over its entire length and breadth: contrasts which were derived from variations in age and geology, in vegetation, in soils, in climate and weather, in bird and fish life, and in aspect, cover and elevation.

New Zealand was an extremely elongated country with a narrow waist. It was more than 1,000 miles from north to south but with no place more than eighty miles from the sea. As a result of its shape the country had an extremely long coastline in relation to its area. The sea with its extensions through fiords, sounds, harbours and tidal rivers was everywhere and contributed to the watery isolation of New Zealand, 1,200 miles from its nearest land-mass neighbour, Australia.

It was also an elevated country. The jagged and year-round snowcapped backbone of the South Island was a broad and massive structure running from southwest to northeast along the entire length of the island and reaching more than 12,000 feet at its highest point. There were another fifteen peaks along its length which reached up through the clouds to over 10,000 feet, all of them higher than the volcanic mass in the centre of the North Island. The southwest to northeast structural orientation of the Southern Alps was continued in the North Island by the alignment of the mountainous chain which rose out of the sea at the island's southern tip and which reached to the

2. *Fiordland: Milford Sound and Mitre Peak*
A landscape of grandeur, wild and unspoiled.

coast in the east. Only the northern half of the North Island leaned to the north-west as a generally narrower and less elevated appendage to the main trend line of the country.

Geologically it was a very young country. The southwestern and north-western corners of the South Island provided the oldest building blocks to which the remainder and much younger structures were attached. The land mass in A.D. 500 was largely the result of great tectonic upheavals during the late Pliocene and Pleistocene which were primarily responsible for the rise of New Zealand's mountain chains in both islands. This period of mountain build-ing set the basic shape and structural alignment of the country although it was the erosion and deposition of material from the mountainous backbones which created many of the landforms and left the highest peaks as remnants of a once much higher and more majestic mountain backdrop.

Wind and wave, snow and ice, and especially running water had sculptured the landscape and smoothed off many of the original features of coast and high country and had formed flat land and valley. Glaciers had scoured and plucked and excavated valleys, leaving the troughs, in which they had rested, ground out by the ice. Invaded by the sea, they formed deep, dark silent fiords in south-western South Island, while running water had filled long fingerlike lakes, mainly on the eastern side of the Alps. Wind and river deposited materials had built up the only extensive area of plains along the eastern coast of the South Island. A host of other rivers, spawned on the backbone of both islands, had created numerous smaller coastal plains on their way to the sea. The hills were deeply dissected by V-shaped valleys, their dissection kept constantly active by ample rainfall and runoff. Much of the country was highly unstable and easily erodible. Volcanism was still actively violent in the North Island. Periodic earthquakes of varying magnitude indicated that land was still being uplifted at a considerable rate and exposed to the elements.

But above all, New Zealand's corrugated surface presented a bush-clad spectacle of green forest cover. An amazing collection of largely endemic tall forest trees, especially podocarps and dicotyledonous species, graced both the deeply weathered residual soils of the North Island and the prevailingly thin and stony mineral soils, loess-carpeted downlands and gravel plains of the South Island.

At a quite general level four quite distinctive landscapes were recognizable in pre-human times. The North Island as a whole formed a fairly homogeneous unit with the major exception of the central core of the island. In the South Island there were sharp contrasts between the eastern and western sides of the alpine chain.

The central volcanic plateau of the North Island was still in its formative stages and was the most violent and awesome area in New Zealand. This was an outstanding sterile treeless country which was quite remarkable in its extent. Early in the Pleistocene Period, shattering eruptions had formed a plateau of rhyolitic rock, some 10,000 square miles in extent, bounded by vertical bluffs and fractured by faulting and warping. This ignimbrite plateau was showered with volcanic ash and pumice to depths of more than 100 feet from a primary source in the vicinity of Lake Taupo, for a period lasting into the first few centuries of the Christian era. In A.D. 500 ash and mud were still being showered over more restricted parts of the plateau's surface. The cumulative effect of the ash showers had burnt and buried the primeval forest, disrupted drainage patterns, and choked rivers and streams for hundreds of years with the yellow-grey ash. The landscape was smothered and subdued by an unconsolidated spread of sterile material which was rapidly eroding and producing a treeless, lifeless, desertlike condition on the elevated plateau of the central North Island. It was an area studded with fumaroles, vents and geysers and characterized by the gurgle of boiling hot water, the splatter of mud pools, the whistle and hiss of steam, and permeated by the distinctive sulphurous smell. Irregular earth tremors, intermittent explosions from active craters, and the pall of choking ash carried from vents, were all signs of a youthful country expending its energies in creating one of the most outstanding areas in New Zealand.

The remainder of the North Island, in comparison with both its central core and the South Island, appeared less spectacular and more subdued. This was not simply a function of its generally lower relief but more because the highly dissected and locally very steep country was disguised and hidden by the dense and continuous cover of damp, dull and drab bush blanket. Apart from the triple formation of volcanic peaks in the centre of the island and their sister cone on the west coast, the North Island's greywacke mountain ranges were completely shrouded in bush. Unlike the South Island there were no major areas of perpetual snow, ice or bare rock to emphasize the ruggedness or elevation of the terrain.

The vegetation of the northern half of the island was dominated by the giant kauri, a tree which reached massive girth and impressive height before branches sprouted to form its regal canopy. South of the kauri a more general mixture of podocarp species predominated. The kahikatea thrived with its feet in the swampy conditions of the damp, wet plains. Rimu, totara, rewarewa, tawa and tanekaha were all prominent species.

The narrow isthmus which joined the northern peninsula to the remainder of the island was studded with volcanic cones, all of them long since dormant except for Rangitoto in the gulf. Explosion craters, tuff rings, rough coarse lava flows and ash deposits formed the greater part of the isthmus. Other volcanic cones with their original shapes but partly intact after years of erosion stretched northeastwards from the west coast of Taranaki to the safety valve of New Zealand at the breached and active crater on White Island in the Bay of Plenty. Northwards the eroded relics of long extinct volcanoes were common features of the pre-human landscape.

The sea had invaded and drowned river valleys to form the shallow land-locked harbours along the northern west coast. The west coast beaches of black iron sand were pounded by the sea, and dunes, hundreds of feet high, were built up along the coastal margins. And everywhere the damp, impenetrable bush, the humid wet weather and the smell of decaying vegetation was the domain of a rich bird life. A deep still silence hung over the country and was broken only by the trickle, splash and gurgle of water and by both harsh and pleasant calls of land and sea birds. The drab green bush cover was relieved in places by the vivid red splash of rata flowers, the golden blooms of the kowhai, the pink-white of the clematis and by other flowering species.

In the South Island the landscape was more spectacular and was dominated by the jagged, snowcapped and bare rocky mountain buttress. To the east of the ranges conditions were a little drier and, apart from the central North Island, this was the largest area where the heavy bush cover did not predominate. The tussock grasslands which were invading the area were later to be induced over a much wider sweep of country but even in pre-human times they were finding a niche in the drier conditions, replacing the former matai-totara forest cover. The eastern plains, built up from the water and wind borne debris from the adjacent mountain range, were the most extensive areas of near flat land in the country. The main agents in their formation, the great rivers which crossed the plains to the sea in the east, were milk-coloured by the glacial melt-water they carried in their wide and gravel-braided courses.

It was on the eastern plains that New Zealand's distinctive and varied bird life was most heavily concentrated. In the absence of terrestrial mammalian predators, insular and isolated New Zealand had developed a highly varied and remarkable fauna of birds. This diversified land-based bird life had survived the vicissitudes of Pleistocene volcanism and climatic change and was chiefly responsible for any grazing or browsing pressures which were being exerted on the indigenous flora. With the lack of competitors many of the bird species had developed heavy flightless forms. The most distinctive were the ratite moas (*Dinornis*) of which two families, six genera and about twenty-five species were present. Great flocks of moas roamed the open tussock, scrub and dying forest thicket in the South Island. They were also present in lesser numbers in both North and Stewart Islands but representatives of almost all the species – nineteen – were found in the South Island. The great ungainly moas ranged in height from 3 to 12 feet with the largest having legs as tall as a man and as stout as an ox. With small, broad, flattened skulls, short bills and ratite, these ostrichlike birds survived primarily on a diet of grass, although fruit, leaves and twigs of forest species were included in their unselective feeding habits.

But the moas were not the only element in the faunal riches of pre-human New Zealand. There was a wealth of other species including the swan, goose, crow, giant rail and eagle as well as the takahe (*Notornis*), kakapo, weka, wood pigeon, quail, kiwi, tui and bellbird. Waterfowl and sea birds including the prized *titi* or mutton-bird further supplemented the diverse avifauna. And the wide range of birds was matched by the diversity of habitats available to them in pre-human New Zealand. Lakes and swamps and lagoons were heavily stocked with geese, swans and ducks; the sand dunes on both east and west coasts and the craggy shore lines were alive with sea birds; the heavy bush appeared to be in constant motion with the movement of terrestrial species both large and small, coloured and drab.

To these riches must be added the coastal waters and sands and mud flats of both islands which were encrusted and embedded with shellfish of all kinds including oysters, pipis, toheroas, scallops, mussels, cockles, crayfish and sea eggs. There were heavily populated rookeries of seals thick on the southern shores. The sea and lagoons, fiords and harbours accommodated a rich fish life; the swamps and creeks eels or tuna; and the coastal waters (especially the narrow straits between the three islands) were visited by schools of right or black whales in the calving season.

The alpine mass and the land to the west of it made up the fourth distinctive

3. *Southern Alps: the Young valley, tributary of the Makarora above Lake Wanaka*

Little modified southern beech forest hangs on the alpine slopes close to the main divide at elevations up to almost 5000 feet.

area of New Zealand. Dominated by the greywacke and schist mountains which formed the anchor stone of the country, the terrain plunged steeply from the jagged snow ridges to the narrow coastal plains of the wet west coast. Unlike the eastern South Island, this area was completely clothed in a heavy bush cover from the dark heaving sea and gravel strewn beaches to the snowline. In the southern portion, the fiords were shut in by precipitous walls of dripping rock faces soaring hundreds of feet from the protected waterways. At the head of valleys high up in the mountains, glaciers pushed and ground their way to both the east and west. The contrast between the heavy green forest canopy and the slash of a sparkling river of ice was striking. This was a wild and remote section of New Zealand which was continually shrouded with swirling rain clouds, cold and bleak and wet.

New Zealand in A.D. 500 was a remote and isolated country. It was the domain of a strange and varied avifauna which had a wide range of forest, grassland, swamp and coastal habitats from which to choose. It was a country of mountains, steep hills and limited areas of coastal plains. But, above all, it was a country kept perpetually wet and dripping by the rains brought from the vast ocean areas which surrounded it. Its remote position in the southern ocean meant that New Zealand's virgin country had to wait until late in the human time scale before man first intruded on the scene to upset and speed up the processes of Nature which had created a unique island environment.

Part Two
The Polynesian impact

Chapter 2
The moahunter landscape

Just exactly when or in what numbers man first arrived in New Zealand no one really knows with any great accuracy. Archaeological evidence gives some clue to a possible time scale but the available C14 dates are sparsely distributed, the sites investigated often fragmentary, and much remains to be done in order to establish a sufficiently comprehensive inventory and to lend confidence to reconstructions of the past.

It is generally accepted that there were two phases in the sequence of pre-European settlement in New Zealand, both based on cultures derived from Eastern Polynesia. The earlier phase was a period of exploitative activities based on the indigenous resources of the country and which supported a relatively small population. The earliest inhabitants are normally referred to as moahunters although it has been suggested that the period during which they were dominant might more accurately be called the Archaic phase of New Zealand Eastern Polynesian culture. Their culture and economy were dominant from, perhaps, A.D. 700 to some time in the fourteenth century, although smaller groups with a moahunter culture may have persisted into the seventeenth century. The second phase has been labelled the Classical Maori period of New Zealand Eastern Polynesian culture and is timed from the arrival of a possible 'Great Fleet' in the middle of the fourteenth century. This Maori culture (and its accompanying material way of life) was 'caught alive' at the height of its development by the earliest scientific explorers and navigators in the late eighteenth century.

Whether the two phases were the result of separate colonizing movements, whether the later phase was the result of evolution from the earlier sequence, or whether they existed side by side and independently of one another during the last four centuries before European man disrupted the scene is not at all clear. Whether one or other or both cultures were the product of deliberate and planned migration to New Zealand, or whether man arrived in much smaller numbers than previously supposed as a result of accidental voyages, is again still subject to debate and speculation. Despite these difficulties, however, it is possible to assess with some assurance what New Zealand was like when the first human settlers arrived, what it was like after a millennium of cultural interference by 'primitive' man and, with less confidence, the extent to which Polynesian man was responsible for the changes in the landscape that had occurred in the intervening time.

There are radio-carbon dates for early settlement sites which indicate that man was firmly established in New Zealand in significant numbers by the middle of the tenth century. Evidence from the South Island suggests that settlements there were thriving organizations a century before this time. How much earlier the first men are to be credited with setting foot in the country depends on whether the number of persons who arrived during that initial period ever becomes known. The fewer canoes arriving, the smaller the absolute numbers, the more imbalanced the proportion of men and women among those who survived the hazardous journey and the longer it took to build up numbers, then the earlier must one project. Dates ranging from the eighth to the tenth century A.D. have so far been proposed as marking the time at which the moahunters were firmly established in New Zealand and it is quite feasible that man was here very much earlier.

When man reached New Zealand either accidentally or deliberately from Eastern Polynesia he was familiar with a mild and restricted tropical environment, comprising coral limestone atoll or high volcanic island. When he arrived in New Zealand he was exposed to an extensive, largely tree-mantled 'continental' range of structures and lithology. As he began his first tentative probings he found the greywackes, mudstones and schists which made up the bulk of the country readily available on beaches, along rivers and on crumbling and exposed bare slopes. In time he discovered the deposits of obsidian (volcanic glass) the primary source of which was Mayor Island, the quartzites and jasperiods of the southern third of the South Island, the fine-grained argillites mainly in the rich mineral belt of Nelson and Marlborough, and the much more restricted but highly prized deposits of nephrite and bowenite on the South Island's remote and almost inaccessible west coast.

At home on his tiny tropical atoll or high island in the central Pacific, Polynesian man was first and foremost an agriculturalist and, secondly, a fisherman. On his arrival in New Zealand his first and most critical task was to survive. Few of his agricultural skills were of immediate use – he could not afford the time to experiment with new and unfamiliar soil types and climatic conditions if he was to live. He was a skilled implement maker and could readily turn his hand to fashioning adzes, spears and knives once he had had time to explore and exploit the greatly expanded universe of which he found himself part. But exploration and testing the new rocks and minerals from which he could manufacture his tools was an exacting and time-consuming task and an activity which, again, had to be relegated to a time when survival was ensured and secured.

New Zealand presented a much cooler climate than that of the central Pacific and many of those who survived the early voyages – especially if the first arrivals were blown off course and landed fortuitously from canoes, ill-prepared for an ocean expedition of such distance – must have been badly prepared to start life afresh in the strange land on which they found themselves cast ashore. It is unlikely, too, that seed kumaras, yams and gourds survived the trip or, if they did, that they were successfully propagated in the new and harsher environment on the first few attempts. However, the new land, its jagged backbone snow-covered, its outline obscured by cloud and rain, contained a grand variety of bird, fish life and forest riches which had the potential to sustain human occupants with comparative ease once man had, or was able to evolve, the techniques to know, catch and cook them.

Presented with a choice between the North and South Islands, existing archaeological evidence and logical deduction both indicate that the South Island was likely to be the more attractive for the early Polynesian settlers. The higher densities and great variety of bird life – especially of moas – the more extensive areas of plain and downland with lighter bush cover and even some open grassland, the presence of seals and whale, a wide range of other sea foods, and the geological variety of the South Island's cooler, frostier terrains, must have appeared more attractive than the warmer but perpetually damp dripping forests, the sterile ash-strewn volcanic areas and the much more dissected and difficult hill country of the North Island. It is likely, too, that the frostier air but clearer skies of eastern South Island, with less rainfall and more abundant sunshine, provided weather and climate sensibly more attractive than that of the warmer but wetter winter months of the North.

Assuming that the earliest arrivals lacked plant material or that the cuttings and tubers they brought with them failed to root in the alien conditions, man must have become a hunter and gatherer during his first few generations in New Zealand. To the hunter, the moa, amongst all the bird species present, became the principal source of protein food, as well as providing material for clothing and implements. It became known to these first people – themselves now called moahunters – as the *kuranui* ('great treasure' or 'primary resource'). The giant bird's flesh was the major item on the irregular, *umu*-cooked menu; the skin the chief material for clothing; the bones a principal raw material for ornaments, fish hooks, spear points, harpoon barbs, minnow shanks, and awls; the eggs a source of both food and pierced-shell water vessels.

There is abundant evidence to indicate that the moa occurred in large numbers in many parts of the country. The frequency and density of remains – bones and crop stones – show that very considerable numbers of these flightless birds grazed grassland, and browsed trees and shrubs in most parts of forested New Zealand, the largest species consuming as much grass as an ox each day.*

* In the Pyramid Valley swamp, in north Canterbury, whole skeletons of the giant birds have been found at a density of 750 to 800 to the acre. At Kopua, Waimate, a swamp deposit yielded 800 moas from an excavation measuring 30 by 20 feet by 8 feet deep. In other parts of the country moa bones have since been carted away by Europeans from similar sites to be crushed at bone mills for fertilizer. And there is evidence that the Maoris themselves mined the bone deposits for raw material from which to fashion fish hooks and other bone instruments.

Although accumulated over many decades, if not centuries, the densities of such deposits are clearly indicative of the size of the moa flocks on which early man came to depend and which he harried and hunted to extinction over a period of perhaps less than a thousand years.

One of the most precious skills man brought with him and which he found of immediate and practical use was his ability to set and make fire. Excavations of moahunter village sites have revealed a plenitude of earthern ovens (*umu*), filled with smooth waterworn stones in which food was cooked. The ovens and surrounds were caked and impregnated with the fatty remains of birds, rats, dogs and seals, and charred bones. Fire was probably critical for domestic heating in the frostier night air of the South Island and in the penetratingly damp chill of the North Island's characteristic succession of winter weather.

In his home islands in the tropical Pacific, the Polynesian had used fire to clear his gardening plots from the heavy tree growth, and he probably found the value of fire in pushing back the forest margins of New Zealand. In this case, however, fire was used not with the intention of providing clearings in which to plant crops, but to drive moas and other flightless creatures to points where they could be more easily dispatched with the tools he had learned to make. The flames, fanned by the desiccating nor'wester which then as now was liable to sweep across the eastern plains from out of the foothills and valleys of the Southern Alps during the hot dry summers, would panic the birds and drive and herd the flocks on to gravel islands in braided rivers, into natural cul-de-sacs, into swamps and on to sandy spits and promontories where the hunter held the advantage over his confined, confused and exhausted quarry.

Over the centuries, the continual use of fire, either deliberately or inadvertently, had a significant and widespread effect on the landscape. It destroyed almost completely the remnant forest in areas where its ecological balance had already become precarious; and it prevented forest regeneration in other places where the local climate still favoured tree growth. The soils of the eastern plains and downlands and basins were peppered with the charcoal remains of a once splendid and thriving forest; the hillsides now covered with wind-tossed bunches of tussock, are dimpled with hollows and mounds left by the rotting of fallen forest giants and their mass of roots; logs and stumps can still be found on the now treeless expanse, both on the littoral and in the mountains inland. Then, as hundreds of years later when the European pastoralist used the induced tussock grasslands to graze his domesticated stock, the Polynesian found that fire and burning stimulated the new 'pastures'. The removal of forest exposed the thin gravel soils of the plains and headwaters to rain and frost and wind, setting off New Zealand's first cycle of manmade erosion. Increased run-off and the increased debris load of the rivers swirled across the plains at melt water season inundating river mouths, burying a forest on the present day site of Christchurch with 12 feet of detritus, and perhaps destroying or entombing moahunter settlements at the mouths of these wild and then uncontrolled waterways.

The hunt for moas had disastrous effects on their numbers. Harried and ravaged by man, their eggs destroyed by fire or claimed by the hunters, the flocks continually threatened and disturbed, and the changing ecological basis on which they had endured for millennia, all contributed to a marked decline in their number. Understandably, the first species to disappear were the largest, most cumbersome and most vulnerable of the birds. Those which survived the longest were driven back to more isolated, remote, elevated and frosty inter-montane basins and the forested areas of Southland and to the interiors of the islands. Several species, including *Euryapteryx gravis* and even one of the largest moas, *Dinornis torosus*, survived in Southland until the seventeenth century. But the growing scarcity of this 'principal resource' was reflected in the increased value placed upon it. Even before A.D. 1250 blown moa eggs were so prized that they were placed in graves along with large adzes and 'whale-tooth' and 'reel' necklaces as burial offerings for adult males of high rank.

The moa was not the only bird to suffer during this sustained attack on New Zealand's once remarkable avifauna. Slowly the moahunter accounted for the extinction of the crow, eagle, rail, goose, swan and species of duck. His midden and refuse piles around the village mirrored the changing composition and availability of birds as increasingly he had to turn to fishing and the collection of shellfish from the rock shores and sandy reaches of the coast, to replace the birds on which he had depended.

The decline in moa numbers and the greater difficulty in capturing them as they retreated inland and became more cautious of man, brought further changes in their wake. The moahunter followed his now indispensable source of food and raw materials into the cooler elevated districts and he carried fire with him. On his forays, away from the coast in quest of the moa, fires were still kindled.

They pushed back the bush margin, leaving it black and ravaged until invaded by tussock grass, shrubs and fire resistant species. Temporary encampments were set up in the interior and the slain birds were conveyed to the permanent settlements on the coast, possibly by rafts down one or other of the rivers leading from the high country. Such temporary centres for the exploitation of the moa would almost certainly be abandoned in winter when sleet and snow drove the hunters back to the relative warmth of the coast, where they would have to depend on fish from the lagoons and sea, eels from the rivers and swamps, smaller birds and rhyzomes grubbed from the soil until they could return to the interior.

To exploit the various mineral resources of the country the moahunter had to range even more widely over a great variety of terrain. What is even more impressive is the widespread distribution of these resources and the frequency with which they were actively used in the coastal hubs of moahunter activity many hundreds of miles from their original source. There was very considerable contact and exchange between the different groups, and a well established 'marketing' system existed to achieve such distributions. Temporary camps were also needed and at the source areas of the prized minerals the precious stones were chipped and flaked to manageable size before being carried by water or on stout backs to coastal settlements. The final stages in the manufacture of adze heads, knives, neck ornaments, spear and harpoon points took place after many laborious hours of patient flaking, fracturing and rubbing to achieve the required shape, balance and sharpness.

All permanent settlement was concentrated along the coast, primarily along the eastern coast of the South Island but with smaller concentrations on the indented coast and islands of the Manukau harbour, the Hauraki gulf, the Coromandel peninsula; along the dune-lined littoral of Taranaki and Horowhenua and about Wellington harbour. Recent reports of sites, as yet unexcavated, suggest a possibly significant concentration on the drier eastern coast of the North Island in Hawkes Bay.

Unlike that of their Maori successors, the moahunters' settlement was an unsophisticated and rudimentary form of shelter. The sites they selected for their more permanent villages or communities were remarkably similar in their characteristics. Most were built on dry spits of shingles or boulders, or on sand dunes adjacent to lagoons or rivermouth estuaries, areas which, although exposed to the wind and cold, were easily accessible along the sheltered waterways or were free from heavy vegetation. Such locations also gave the moahunters ready access to fish and bird life, to a plentiful supply of firewood from logs grounded at rivermouths and from driftwood cast ashore along beach frontages. When the moas grazed the grasslands nearby at the onset of settlement, such sites on spits provided natural cul-de-sacs into which the birds could be driven and killed close to the camp.

The shelters the moahunters erected to protect them from the elements were constructed of perishable materials, and all that remain are occasional postholes, fireplaces and collections of prized articles. Littering the camp site were the relics and rubbish of the moahunters' daily diet and round of life: moa and other bird bones, blown moa egg shells, middens thickly strewn with an assortment of shellfish, bones of seals and whales and fish, fatty impregnated ashes cleared from the ovens and cast nearby, flakes and splinters from the rocks they fashioned for their implements; and some of the implements themselves – adzes, knives, scrapers, minnow shanks, fish hooks, spear points, needles, awls and perhaps some of the ornamental necklaces of bones or precious minerals.

The moahunter was kept too busy with the task of acquiring knowledge of his new environment and of surviving by hunting and gathering to spend time on aggressive warfare. He did not need weapons of war. His village was unfortified and his dead buried without fear of molestation. The extent to which mineral resources were distributed and exchanged meant frequent and friendly contact with a chain of neighbouring camps. Mutton-birds, potted and preserved in their own fat, quartzite and nephrite formed the 'currency' for the southernmost settlements to acquire North Island obsidian and northern South Island argillites.

Just what numbers were supported by the moahunter economy is not known. Various estimates place the figure in the vicinity of 10,000 to 15,000. On the basis of the number and size of known settlements this means that at its peak in the thirteenth century between 8,000 and 12,000 Polynesian men and women inhabited and lived in the South Island. The population of the South Island did not reach this total again until the Canterbury and Otago settlements were founded in the middle of the nineteenth century.

The middle of the fourteenth century marks the decline of the moahunter as the dominant ecological agent in New Zealand, as the new wave of Polynesian migrants claimed territory and superimposed their culture on that which had preceded it. Concentrated much more in the North Island, it was a culture which possessed superior skills and techniques, one which became aggressive and warlike in its attitude and had an economy characterized by the cultivation of kumara or sweet potato and other crops.

The moahunter's contribution to the New Zealand landscape, however, still persists. At the end of his occupation of the eastern South Island, he had transformed a landscape dominated by a variety of forest and scrub vegetation into one of expansive grassland rarely interrupted except by minor shrub and tree species. Not less than 8 million acres of matai-totara forest had been destroyed by fire and replaced by tussock and scrub. Accelerated erosion had infilled valleys and depressions, choked rivers and modified the coastline where the debris was spewed forth to the sea. Despite his relatively small numbers and despite his rather crude and primitive skills and technology, the moahunter was a potent force in harnessing and changing the natural landscape of early New Zealand. Largely through his efforts, one of the most distinctive and significantly different regions of New Zealand had already been cleared of forest and converted to grassland. This was 600 or 700 years before the European gratefully accepted what he thought to be 'natural' pastures as a vital basis of his pioneer economy.

Chapter 3
The Maori landscape

Sometime between A.D. 1200 and 1400 New Zealand was invaded by another Polynesian group from the northeast – the Maori. Arriving in a number of large, specially prepared oceangoing canoes over a period of perhaps 200 years, this incursion has become known as the Great Fleet. Whether New Zealand at this time experienced a sustained and planned period of migration involving significant numbers, or whether there ever was a Great Fleet as such, is not as important to the present consideration as the fact that about this time man-made changes were brought about in the landscape.

The patterns of occupance and economy which the Maori built were in marked contrast to those of the moahunters. At the peak of its development the Maori population totalled twenty to twenty-five times the number of moa-hunters who had inhabited the country centuries before. The Maori was over-whelmingly concentrated in the North Island, with fewer than 10 per cent of his numbers in the moahunters' former domain to the south. Unlike the moa-hunter, the Maori was to a considerable extent a conservationist who managed and planned the utilization of the land and its resources through a rigid system of *tapu*. In the northern half of the North Island where his numbers were more tightly concentrated the settlements he built became sophisticated architec-tural and engineering achievements, and his economy was based largely on crops introduced from the islands of the central Pacific.

Like the moahunter, it took the Maori at least several generations to explore and assess the new environment, to experiment and to establish his crops and to get to know fish, fowl, flax, and fern root in an alien environment very different from the one he had left behind in the tropics. For much of the time during the first century or so after his arrival in New Zealand, the Maori was fully engaged in a struggle for existence. Until he perfected the skills, tools and techniques that enabled him to utilize more fully the resources of his new home, the Maori lived in village communities near the most valuable resources (forest, river, fertile soil, swamp or sea) of the particular locale in which he chose to live. His settlements were open, unfortified villages called *kainga*. Each settlement was the home of a subtribe (*hapu*) claiming descent from one of the oceangoing canoes which set out from the islands, far to the northeast, with the purpose of finding and colonizing New Zealand.

The successful introduction of crops, sensitive to climate and soils, meant the

Maori's assessment of the country's potential and promise differed from that of the moahunter. He settled in the warmer, more humid and wetter areas of the North Island. Coastal locations with their ameliorating effects on temperatures were also important. It was the 'winterless' northern peninsula, the volcanic isthmus of Auckland and its surrounding islands in the Hauraki gulf, the Coromandel peninsula, the Waikato river valley, the littoral between Waihi and Whakatane on the east and the rich volcanic coast of Taranaki on the west which proved most suitable and where the bulk of the population settled. Lesser concentrations developed around Lakes Taupo, Rotorua and Waikaremoana, along the Wanganui river and the coast of Horowhenua, and in the Waimea and Wairau valleys and at Kaiapohia (Kaiapoi) in the South Island. In effect, the further inland or the further south the Maori penetrated the more critical conditions became for his crops and the tougher the winning of a livelihood. In particular, Maori numbers in the South Island remained small.

The *kumara* or sweet potato was the most tolerant of those plants successfully introduced and was grown as far south as the eastern littoral of the South Island probably to the vicinity of Temuka. The taro, yam and gourd were more sensitive to climate but formed an important part of the diet in the northern frost-free areas. In addition, the Maori established the paper mulberry, and he may also have introduced the ti palm (*Cordyline terminalis*) and the karaka. Because the balance between success and failure was much finer in the new land, the Maori had to become adept at selecting the right seasons and areas for his crops. He had names for at least thirty different soil types, and he greatly modified some which were not immediately suitable for his purposes by carrying large quantities of sand in flax baskets over long distances to mix with and lighten the heavier, stickier clays. He also used fire to burn the vegetation cover, and brought charcoal and brush for firing from other areas to spread on the topsoil and to add to the fertility of the soils.

In the Waikato valley, thousands of acres of bush were cleared over the decades, the vegetation fired patch by patch, and sand and charcoal worked into the plots so that the upper soil horizons were peppered with man-induced ingredients long before the *pakeha* applied his steel axe and plough to what was considered virgin country. In the Waimea valley, Nelson, the Maori laboriously and painstakingly removed thousands of tons of gravel to lighten the heavy soils for kumara gardens. Over the years he excavated pits 3 to 10 acres in extent, in his patient and devoted efforts to increase the production from his plots.

Such efforts are impressive when one is reminded of the primitive tools he possessed with which to cultivate the land – the *ko* or digging stick which Cook described as a 'stout picket', and simple wooden grubbing and scraping implements. Like his moahunter predecessor, he 'cropped' the fern root (*aruhe*) as a major staple and his search for it led him to probe and break the soil over wide areas. In the areas most suited to crops – especially on the red volcanic and light pumice alluvial soils of the north – Maori cultivation was relatively fixed. The plots, or gardens, were laid out in family groups, subdivided with stones and tracks and protected from prevailing winds by manuka brushwood barriers. A rigid system of *tapu* as decreed by the *tohunga*, or by the elders, set down the planting and harvesting times and ensured that abundant food was available at all times. Work was communal and labour divided according to the task requiring to be done. A group of warriors was set to fell the smaller trees with their primitive adzes and to drag up the brushwood and dried logs in preparation for firing. A line of men armed with the *ko* were needed to inch their way across a plot, jabbing the soil and levering clods of earth which later would be broken and hoed for the planting. Women and children were employed to remove sticks and stones and to pile them along boundaries forming rough fences.

In those areas where soils and climate were less suitable, cultivation played a less important role and tended more to the traditional form of bush clearing by fire and by constantly shifting the plots, leaving them finally to be reclaimed once more by the damp aggressive bush. Gathering and hunting, rather than cultivating foods, contributed the more significant portion of the diet in such areas as the forested mountain retreats of the Urewera and the cool and exposed plateau near Lake Taupo. This form of activity, combined with shifting agriculture, was more in keeping with the traditions practised in the Pacific home islands; but even in the areas of more intensive cultivation, gathering and hunting and fishing consumed the Maori's time, energy and ingenuity.

The Maori had knowledge of the migration of various fish as they moved to spawning grounds and he used this knowledge both to increase his catch and to guarantee supply by banning fishing at the spawning season. Skilfully woven nets were strung across creeks and tidal inlets to trap flounder and kahawai, canoes were taken out to sea or out into the harbours and line fishing with finely etched bone hooks was practised. Mussels, oysters, sea eggs and crayfish were plucked from the rocky coasts or dived for in the shallower coastal water. Pipis, cockles, crabs, periwinkles, toheroas and scallops were dug and scratched from the sand and mud by women and carted back to the village in flax baskets. Ingenious baskets or traps 'manufactured' from pliable sticks and twigs were submerged in swamps and creeks to catch eels.

In the bush around the village, the dense growth masked a hive of activity. The forest was brought to life by the crash of a stately totara being felled by workers preparing a suitable log for a canoe or for a building, by the stealthy movement of hunters as they flitted through the forest shadows in search of birds or rats or as they set cunningly contrived snares for pigeons, bellbirds, tuis and other birds. Another group was patiently engaged in hacking or burning out a log to create the shell of a canoe.

In the village itself, other men were engaged in digging holes for the posts which formed the framework of a sleeping hut or meeting house; others carefully and skilfully carving the elaborate designs to grace a barge board or lintel for the *whare* or house. Groups of women were busy plaiting mats, baskets, wall panels, preparing food in the 'kitchens' over wood fires, or curing skins and weaving fibres for clothing. Much of the work, apart from the most mundane and routine, was supervised by the *tohungas* and elders standing aside clothed in their bird feather cloaks.

In the same way as the moahunter, the Maori exploited the geological riches of the country for his adzes, spears, necklaces and knives. To a greater extent than his predecessor, he treasured and used more extensively the nephrite or greenstone (*pounamu*) of the South Island's wet west coast and a considerable trade grew up focused on this area. Obsidian, quartzite and argillites as well as bones – both human and others – were also utilized for fashioning into hooks, awls, ornaments, spear points and adze heads.

Regular routeways were developed connecting the riches and treasures of the different parts of the country with the sites of their use and consumption. The large protected harbours of the Kaipara, Manukau and Waitemata were linked by portages. The inland waterways of the Waikato, Waipa and Wanganui rivers served as major arteries for people on social and trading ventures, while the black sandy beaches of the west coast formed significant 'highways' for foot traffic. A quick dash by canoe across Cook Strait, on a relatively fine and calm day, put the greenstone and mutton-birds of the South Island within reach of the northern tribes, and a voyage from the Waihi-Tauranga coast placed the Mayor Island obsidian deposits at their disposal.

But the Maori's impact on the landscape, during the early years when he led a peaceful existence, was not as lasting or as significant as that of the moahunter. To clear the wet impenetrable bush cover of the North Island by fire was a completely different task from putting torch to the drier open forest cover of the eastern South Island. It was difficult to get a good burn and, once a cleared plot had been abandoned, the aggressive vegetative growth soon covered over its scars with a dense greenery which greedily reasserted its rights and, within a few years, virtually erased man's tentative touch from sight or sign. He built channels in swamp and creek to assist his eeling; he cut down a few large trees for his canoes and buildings; he hunted, gathered and fished but always within the limits imposed by the *tapu* and an inherent reverence for Nature. His keen sense of conservation meant that he made little long-term impression on the land's surface.

However, once he was firmly established in the country and had mastered its difficulties, the Maori found himself with greater time on his hands and turned to other pursuits. Initially, a wide range of games and skills were developed in the village for leisure and as tests of manhood; they took up the warrior's time but soon led to occasional forays on neighbours to right some real or imagined insult or trespass, and then to warfare on a wide scale. Once this state had been reached – especially among the larger more powerful tribes of heavily populated northern areas where fertility and resources made planting more productive – open village sites were no longer adequate, and the Maori turned his attention and very considerable energies and talents to constructing elaborate defensive positions. *Kainga* were replaced by *pa*. Massive and extensive earthworks marked the presence of these fortress constructions which even today are the most obvious legacy of the Maori in the New Zealand landscape.

The needs of defence meant that the *hapu* had carefully to select strategic sites which were often some distance from its traditional and established agricultural plots, favourite forest resources or chosen fishing grounds. The *pa* were built on isolated hill sites (the smaller tuff, scoria and lava cones were ideal), on ridges, spurs, coastal headlands, cliffs, offshore islands, river terraces and even on small islands in the swamps. In the northern half of the North Island, hundreds of such sites were selected and occupied. If, as frequently happened, the sites were not ideally suited for *pa* construction then the hillside was sculptured, trenched, terraced and pallisaded to assist the tribe in its defence against aggressive neighbours. Tons of earth and loose rock were shifted by scrapers and crude trowels and carried in baskets to fill in, build up, remove or create obstacles as part of the defensive system. Logs were brought on stout backs or by water from miles around to be fitted into post holes and lashed together to form an intricate system of palisades. And food had to be smoked, dried or preserved and stored along with water in case of siege.

The Tamaki isthmus – an area of very considerable strategic and agricultural value – had twenty-two *pa* sites on its volcanic cones, headlands, adjacent islands and swamps during the course of its occupancy as various tribes struggled to make secure their claim to it. Living now predominantly in the *pa* the Maori often erected temporary shelters near their garden plots, forests and fishing places. With frequency of skirmishing, especially in the winter months, and the need to be continually prepared for attack or retaliation, gardens were often less carefully tended, or were abandoned, as the warriors had to devote more time to fashioning increasingly elaborate weapons of war, to building massive war canoes, to erecting a new *pa* to replace one that had been sacked and razed, to lookout duty or to raids they themselves pursued.

Whatever its configuration or defensive works, the *pa* had a characteristic collection of buildings and a form which repeated in detail the internal morphology of the old-time *kainga*. The grassy or earth-trodden *marae* (village green) was the focal point and the centre of all activity. Around the *marae* in irregular groups were the *wharepuni* which formed the sleeping quarters of loosely extended family groups. The *wharepuni* were simple rectangular structures about 10 by 12 feet with excavated clay or earth floors. They were built with poles or posts and lined with reeds or fronds of tree ferns. The sleeping quarters were cramped and crowded, poorly ventilated by a small window and low door opening on to a gabled verandah which served as an outdoor living space.

The largest and most striking feature in the village, with its elaborate ornamentation, was the *whare runanga*, the meeting house or carved house – the Maori equivalent of the village hall. This was placed at the end of the *marae* opposite the main entry and it dominated both the village and its social life. Rectangular in shape and with the same style of front verandah as the *wharepuni*, the meeting house had deep, intricately carved barge boards, a thatched roof, panelled interior, decorated walls and carved jambs and lintel shields. It was the place where meetings were held and where visitors were housed; and it was the overt expression of the high level of material culture which the Maori achieved.

At the same end of the *marae* and close by the meeting house were the dwellings of the tribal elders and *tohunga*. These were generally more elaborately constructed and decorated than the *wharepuni* of the common warriors. Scattered about were the crude, often unroofed structures which served as cooking sheds or kitchens where the fish and birds and vegetables were prepared and cooked over wood fires. Finally, the *pataka*, or storehouses, were also distinctive. Some were profusely carved structures elevated on one or more posts while others were simple raised platforms or racks and others again were semi or wholly buried pits. The season's harvest of kumaras and yams was stored here along with smoked fish and eels, dried fish, preserved and pickled birds in gourds, together with other food reserves to last through the winter.

The *pa* was enclosed by a complex system of palisading – high fences of pointed tree trunks woven together to form a tight wall – trenches, earthworks, lookout towers and terracing. The fortress was also built so that it comprised a number of separate units or levels – if one section was breached the defenders could fall back on the innermost ring of the stockade.

The wars which were waged, even before the acquisition of firearms from the early Europeans, were ruthlessly and viciously and cunningly planned and executed. When a *pa* was overthrown the women and children were taken prisoner, warriors killed, slaves recruited and the captured fortress destroyed and abandoned. Cannibalism was a common practice. The Tamaki isthmus, one of the most heavily populated and sought after areas at the beginning of the seventeenth century, was completely abandoned and deserted by the time the European came to settle. The cost of defending the rich volcanic soils at Tamaki and its strategic portages between the Tasman and Pacific, was too much for the tribes and they were forced to leave it as a 'no man's land', its volcanic cones terraced and pitted but unoccupied, its rich soils uncultivated and reoccupied by scrub and secondary growth, its fish and bird life once more umolested.

Outside the heavily populated northern area, isolation and distance kept the tribes relatively free from warfare and the *kainga* was retained as the primary village form. The need to devote greater time to winning a livelihood and the lack of a defensive system meant that when occasionally one of the northern tribes came south to plunder the southerners were quickly overthrown.

At the close of the period of Maori supremacy in New Zealand, the population probably numbered at least 250,000. The Maoris' undisputed reign lasted about 400 years and yet in that time their skilful utilization of resources left little tangible evidence of their presence. Only the great terraced *pa* sites remain to remind us of a populous and virile people who explored, experimented and utilized but made slight and rather temporary modifications to Aotearoa's landscapes.

Part Three
The European transformation

Chapter 4
The pioneer landscape

In the two centuries since European man began the sustained exploitation of New Zealand the landscape has been the scene of a series of events which have brought about major changes to the environment he inherited. Like his moa-hunter and Maori predecessors, the European has assessed the usefulness of various parts of the country in different ways at different times. As circumstances, needs and technology changed, so man has re-evaluated the resources New Zealand offered. As a result, the history of European development has witnessed the changing fortunes of North and South Islands, and of specific areas within the two islands, as first one and then the other became the focus of exploitation for a few decades until another innovation set in motion a new cycle of change and development in different parts of the country.

Not all change, of course, has been for the better. Much of the country's endemic fauna and flora has been damaged, destroyed, decimated or reduced to isolated and remote retreats where it survives as a mere fragment and reminder of a richness and splendour with which the country was formerly endowed. So, too, the relentless and reckless removal of a natural vegetation has exposed the thin mantle of soil on hundreds of square miles of steep slopes; slopes and soils which were rapidly washed, reduced and wasted by gully, sheet and wind erosion and mass movement to choke rivers and streams and render useless once briefly productive areas.

But the speed with which the country was tamed and robbed by the settlers' axe, fire, stock, pasture, plough, pan, sluice, tracks, roads and rails is the most spectacular element in New Zealand's short history of European development. Other than on the largely man-induced tussock grasslands of the eastern South Island and the ash-mantled and stunted vegetation of the inaccessible and remote central North Island, the early European must at times have felt quite helpless when faced with the almost hopeless task of converting the New Zealand countryside to his needs. High rainfall, steep – often precipitous – slopes, dense, tall and giant trees, a tangled thicket of ferns, creepers and lianas beneath the 'bush' canopy, deeply entrenched fast-flowing rivers or wide braided gravel channels, young and basically infertile and unstable soils, a country subject to volcanism and earthquakes and inhabited by an unpredictable and for a time antagonistic native population – all these features made the change wrought by the European largely within the last century quite remarkable.

4. *North Island hill country. Inland Taranaki*
Most of the North Island landscape was like this until the European cleared its mixed rainforest in the half century after 1880.

Perhaps even more significant is the fact that, over all, the contemporary patterns of settlement, agriculture and communications were established by the turn of the century. The last half century has really seen a consolidation and intensification and refinement of these patterns rather than new developments or major modifications, although there have been local areas of advance or retreat, progress or stagnation, change and specialization.

Abel Tasman is credited as the first European discoverer of *Aotearoa* – the land of the long white cloud – in 1642, but it was not until a century and a quarter later that Captain James Cook's much publicized voyage of 1768–69 brought word of the riches of New Zealand to England and Europe. Cook was followed by other scientific explorers and navigators, then by sealers, whalers, missionaries, traders and, finally, the first of the colonists in 1840. Since then immigration has been sustained, and permanent settlement the primary aim of most new arrivals.

The first recorded semipermanent incursion of Europeans onto the New

Zealand stage took place in 1792 when a sealing gang of forty men was landed at Dusky Sound, Fiordland, in the South, or Middle, Island as it was known for much of the nineteenth century. A period of almost fifty years followed during which the country was violently raped of its seal and cachalot whale population, and many of its majestic kauri and other native trees were cut and carried off as 'spars' in sailing vessels. As word of the resources spread, so a steady increase took place in the number of vessels calling at New Zealand to trade with the Maori for flax, potatoes, pork and timber. In 1814 the first missionaries arrived with all the good will in the world, but with disastrous results, as they changed the Maori way of life by breaking the old traditions and by introducing the Polynesian to new stock and crops and agricultural methods. Less tangible as an expression in the landscape, but just as violent, was the impact of the *pakeha* on Maori numbers. Changes in diet, the succumbing to new diseases, the acquisition of firearms, the abandonment of the traditional way of life and place of living, all resulted in a quite cataclysmic reduction in Maori population.

The sealing grounds were largely concentrated in the far south, along the Murihiku-Otakau (Southland-Otago) coast. Here on the wild rocky shore swept by wind and wave, shrouded in mist and rain, and bitterly cold in winter, the temporary encampments of sealers were established. The seals on this stretch of the coast were reported as being thick on the ground and their capture a simple matter. By 1810 the rookeries on the mainland had been almost completely exterminated and for a few years the area was more or less abandoned.

From as early as 1794 whaling vessels, searching the southern ocean for the sperm or cachalot whale, had been making regular calls at the Bay of Islands for refitting and victualling. After about thirty years pelagic whalers were replaced by establishments of bay and shore whalers who sought the right or black whale. This led to a new series of more permanent settlements along the coast near where the whales came to calve. By the late 1820s the Murihiku-Otakau coast was again studded with camps, while Cook Strait and the Bay of Islands were also populated by shore whalers. The beach at each encampment was characterized by the tryworks for raising the whale by block and tackle to strip it of its blubber, the trypots for boiling it down, the barrels and cooperage, the boatsheds and long boats, the stench of whale oil and burning scragg, the litter of bones and the crude huts of the whalers, some of whom by now had Maori 'wives'.

During this period the exploitation of seals, whales, timber and Maori was largely confined to the littoral. A few straggling settlements of quasipermanent trade centres, inhabited by a miscellaneous collection of Europeans and pakeha-Maoris, attached themselves to the coastline in favoured areas. The largest such settlement was at Kororareka in the Bay of Islands – a settlement infamous in the Pacific at this date for its wild and lawless collection of riffraff made up of whalers, ships' deserters, escapees from the Australian penal centres and by other social misfits. The stores, the taverns, rum shops and mean dwellings serviced and housed a population of about 1,000 in the late 1830s.

The only group to brave the interior of the wild and largely unknown North Island, where many of the Maoris lived, were the missionaries. They quickly established a chain of mission stations in the Waikato basin and along the coast of the Bay of Plenty and inland to Rotorua. Their efforts to stamp out warfare among the tribes, to abolish slavery and discredit cannibalism, while at the same time introducing different agricultural crops and techniques, had profound effects in undermining a culture which previously had been sensitively adjusted to its forest environment.

The toll taken by influenza, tuberculosis, venereal disease, measles and other introduced illnesses contributed to the sharp decline of the Maori. So, too, did the introduction of flour, sugar, tobacco and alcohol. But the acquisition of firearms gave the Maori a much more effective and efficient weapon of war. This was directly responsible for many deaths in intertribal clashes. In 1769 the Maori population probably numbered in excess of 250,000. This had been reduced by 1840 to about 120,000.

At the same time the incentive to acquire European material goods in the form of blankets, axes, textiles, matches, fish hooks and especially firearms encouraged the Maori to live near embryo trade centres, to abandon his gardens in favour of collecting and preparing the timber, flax and foods the trader wanted, to depend increasingly on imported foods and to ignore his cultural legacy in favour of a supposedly better way of life in the hovels and shanties around the beachheads of the European invasion.

In 1840 two almost simultaneous events – the establishment of the first of the New Zealand Company settlements under the Wakefield plan of colonization and the formal annexation of New Zealand as a British colony – ushered in the beginnings of planned settlement and a period of systematic development. The capital was lodged temporarily at Russell in the Bay of Islands until Governor Hobson selected that part of the Auckland isthmus facing the Waitemata harbour as its site late in 1840. From that time on, with the exception of the years from 1861 to 1886 when Dunedin was the largest centre of population, Auckland has always held the lead as the major city in the country, although it soon lost its capital status.

Wellington was the site selected for the first New Zealand Company settlement and during the next ten years this was followed by settlements at New Plymouth, Nelson, Otago and Canterbury. In this first decade of orderly development, however, it was the North Island that progressed most rapidly and by 1853 had two-thirds of the European population.

But the advances that were made in that first decade were not spectacular. In general, it was a period during which the new settlers had to experiment and reassess their attitudes and techniques for breaking in the new country so vastly different from the long-established English and Scottish homeland. Only Auckland had made any real progress on the rich volcanic soils of the largely treeless isthmus inherited from a previously densely populated Maori community. The productive soils, the ease of clearing and establishing crops and pastures, the availability of fine kauri stands ten miles to the west in the Waitakeres, the large Maori population in its environs, the ease of communications with its harbours, rivers, and creeks, and over its portages and rolling countryside, allowed Auckland to achieve an early lead over the other settlements. By 1853 it had a population of 8,000 and its harbours were busy thoroughfares for overseas and coastal traffic and for more than 2,000 Maori canoes which entered annually. It was self-sufficient in basic foods and was exporting wheat, flour, dairy produce and other goods from its 17,000 acres of cropland. The administrative, military and missionary centre of the country, Auckland was functionally and socially quite different from the more southerly settlements.

New Plymouth had made but slow progress during the same time and only 2,000 settlers were recorded in 1853. They had not yet found an efficient means of clearing the bush-covered lower slopes of the cone-shaped Mount Egmont, and unrest among the Maoris in the area restricted progress and confined the spread of settlers to the initial site and immediate bracken-covered environs. Wheat proved remarkably successful and was being exported to Australia at a time when that country's gold rushes were providing a ready market for any foodstuffs its nearest neighbour could produce.

Wellington suffered in the first few years from a too-hasty selection of site at Petone and the settlement had to be transferred to Lambton harbour to gain greater shelter and to avoid the flood waters of the Hutt river. By 1853 the population had reached 7,000 and the settlers, having overcome earlier Maori intolerance of their presence, were beginning to penetrate the bush-covered hills confining the harbour and to push north. The steep hills around the harbour were not suitable for cropping, and the residents were at this stage heavily dependent on supplies of food from Maoris.

Nelson, too, experienced early difficulties, but the attractiveness and fertility of the Waimea plain was a pointer to future development in the South Island. Both the Otago and Canterbury settlements were barely established by 1853 but settlers were already beginning to turn inland to the expansive yellow tussock country of the plains and interior basins.

Until the 1850s the east coast of both islands had been virtually ignored, but during that decade a new cycle of development was initiated. The next fifty years were undoubtedly the most significant in transforming the face of the land; and though both islands gained from the development that took place, it was a period in which the South Island was clearly ascendant. It was a period when a grass, grain and gold economy gave tremendous impetus to the development of the south, and when the heavy, bush-covered country and increasing hostility of the Maori retarded progress in the North Island.

A series of land laws initiated under Sir George Grey in the 1850s were instrumental in breaking down the philosophy underlying the Wakefield scheme of allocating land, and provided the incentive for the southern settlements to burst out of their previously confined areas and to rampage over the plains and downlands gobbling up vast acreages in the Australian squatter tradition. The grass and fernclad areas of the Wairarapa and Hawke's Bay and especially the great eastern plains, downlands and basins of the South Island were trodden and grazed by herds of cattle and very much larger flocks of sheep. Between 1856 and 1876 more than 8 million acres of land were sold by the provincial governments, $2\frac{1}{4}$ million acres were given away under various systems of free grant, and by 1881 more than 12 million acres of Crown land were leased as great mountain sheep runs, mainly in Canterbury and Otago. In 1853 there were less than half a million sheep in the colony; by 1881 there were 13 million. Exports of wool in 1853 were worth £66,000 but by 1881 the value of wool shipped had risen to more than £3 million. Australian pastoralists with their Merino flocks led the way to be joined later by squatters from England and Scotland.

But the techniques adopted by the pastoralists in the still young country were largely thoughtless and short-term. The first graziers were confronted with an endless carpet of yellow-brown wind-ruffled tussock covering much of the South Island's eastern plains, downs and interior basins. The tussocks were found to be largely unpalatable but the sheltered grasses, herbs and sedges below and among the tussock clumps proved good value. Fire was the key. A good burn, fanned by the föhnlike nor'wester, would destroy the mat of dead tussock leaves and send billowing clouds of smoke rolling across the foothills and plains, and make the new sprouting grasses, sedges and herbs available to foraging stock and promote a fresh green growth. The tussock grazing areas were stocked with more and more Merinos, the burns became more frequent, the tussock less virile. Larger and larger areas of thin, light, stony soils between the tussocks were exposed to wind and rain and frost, rabbits competed with sheep for tender new growth, and the carrying capacity of the 30,000 to 50,000 acre runs deteriorated.

Sheep grazing on indigenous grassland thus provided the initial impetus for the South Island's development and dotted the landscape with the homesteads, woolsheds, yards and pens, shearers' quarters and huts for mustering gangs. The large runs meant a population of from ten to thirty clustered around the homesteads, each run physically separated from the next by wide, gravel-filled braided river channels, by the foothills of the Alps and by distance and slow means of transport.

In contrast to this extensive form of economic activity, the South Island also witnessed a highly concentrated invasion, locally confined and lasting little more than a decade, after the discovery of gold in the Tuapeka valley, Otago, by Gabriel Read in 1861. Gold had been found in the north in 1852, in the kauri-clad hills of the Coromandel peninsula, but the hostile Maoris of the area prevented further prospecting until 1862 when the district was proclaimed a goldfield. The first payable goldfield at Collingwood, Nelson, opened in 1857 but the great attraction of the Australian fields turned attention elsewhere and by 1861 the Nelson field had produced only 41,872 ounces.

Gabriel Read's discovery was made known in June 1861, and by the end of December that year 187,696 ounces of gold had been produced at Tuapeka. The population of Otago had increased in six months from 12,000 to 30,000. This heralded the gold rushes of New Zealand and in the ten years 1861 to 1871 the European population of the country increased two and a half times, from 99,000 to 256,000. From 1862 to 1870 gold comprised 50 to 70 per cent of the value of New Zealand exports, and in the decade following it contributed 20 to 40 per cent annually.

The discovery of payable quantities of gold on the old river terraces and black sandy beaches of Westland in 1864 led to another stampede as miners surged from the Otago fields to the new area of hope. Later still, in 1867, the Thames quartz field, centred on Waihi and the Coromandel peninsula, got under way and helped sustain the export flow of precious metal. The Thames area, however, offered much less scope to the individual prospector, requiring large inputs of capital, machinery and labour to win the ore in contrast to the simpler methods employed in the extraction of the southern alluvial deposits and the crude stamper batteries erected to crush the quartz from the Otago schist.

Quite apart from the boost gold gave to the youthful export economy, its impact was felt in numerous facets of the country's life and reflected in its landscapes. The great surge of miners seeking the precious metal swelled the number of settlers as many chose to remain after the rushes were over. Because the fields had never been fully prospected before the rushes set in and their extent was thus unknown, the miners blazed trails through much of the almost unexplored basin, gorge and mountain interior of Otago, across the ragged, snow-capped Alps and along the narrow coastal plain and foothills of the wild and wet and forested West Coast. With his spade, pick and washing pan, the digger pushed his way through wet and tangled bush, frosted tussock grass, along river valleys, over precipice and mountain range, into the loneliest and most inaccessible parts of the country. When he found gold in what promised to be payable quantities the sluice boxes were set up, streams dammed, 'paddocks' of auriferous gravel excavated, tunnels driven into terraces and hillsides, and timber cut for props and rough shelters and firewood. If a really rich strike was made, hydraulic mining might be attempted. Water races were constructed and water led along them to the mining site where jets were directed to tear away the mass of loose stony river-deposited detritus and to wash the gravels into sluice boxes and tail races where the gold could be recovered. Although the hydraulic sluicing in particular rendered hundreds of acres desolate and forlorn as the country was stripped and denuded, it was generally carried on in places too remote, barren and broken to be of much account for any other purpose.

Gold mining did not suddenly die after the decade of headlong hectic rushes. Much of the country had been passed over in the first stampede with but a cursory attempt to probe its surface for mineral riches. In the 1870s the industry became much more settled as the fields were again worked over more systematically both by large organizations employing more sophisticated techniques and machinery and by individuals. The ubiquitous worker of the goldfields, the Chinaman, appeared in New Zealand as the 'gleaner of the fields', and more than 3,000 Chinese fossicked among the debris of former 'digs' to earn a living in the mid-1870s.

When the strike was rich the calico tent and rough-hewn shanty town sprang up to service the miners' needs only to be as hastily deserted a few years later and left to crumble and decay and become yet another ghost town. At least 165 new 'urban' settlements were added to the map of the South Island as a result of the gold rushes which ebbed and swirled up river valleys like the Shotover, Clutha and Arrow and along the beaches and terraces between the Grey and Hokitika rivers on the West Coast.

As early as 1863 the forerunner of the modern gold dredge appeared in the Dunstan area in Central Otago as a crude raft of barrels with an iron-tipped leather bucket attached to a pole for recovering the river sands. In the 1880s steam power was applied to the bucket line so that the dredge could work anywhere in the river regardless of current. Much later, 1899, there were seventy-three dredges working in Otago and Southland in addition to which there were four under removal and nine standing unused with a further thirty under construction or projected – 116 in all. Several dredges were also working the West Coast and as these mechanical miners became larger and more efficient their passage could be marked by the acreages of gravel tailings which were dumped and discarded after the gold was extracted.

Dunedin, of course, as the port of entry for many of the fortune seekers and as the centre of supplies for the feverish activity on the fields, reaped most from the mineral harvest. In 1853 it had a population of dispirited and dissenting Scots who were battling the damp and chilly climate from their tiny daub and wattle cottages, roofed with tussock or shingles, as they tried to establish a viable settlement on the Otago coastline. The town had struggled to a population of 6,349 by 1861 but in 1864 it had been inundated by 15,790 residents most of whom were directly or indirectly benefiting from the mining activities in the hinterland. By 1881 Dunedin had grown to 45,000 – not much less than half its present population – and was the largest city in the colony. It was a city with substantial public and commercial buildings constructed in Oamaru limestone and its rectangular pattern of streets paved and lighted. It had become the headquarters of many of New Zealand's commercial and manufacturing firms.

The sudden influx of prospectors created a new market for agricultural produce and farmers were stimulated to increase and diversify their crop production to meet the demand. In the South Island the area under grain crops increased fourfold between 1861 and 1867. This was a precursor of the changes which were to occur on a grand scale a few years later in the eastern South Island farming system.

Following rapidly on the heels of the mining boom came a major agricultural revolution, initiated by the construction of public works under Vogel's policy of capital borrowing. In 1870, when the colony was feeling the disheartening effects of the Maori wars (then more or less ended), the Colonial Treasurer, Vogel, promulgated his now famous public works programme under which some £10 million of British capital was borrowed and expended on the encouragement of immigration, the construction of railways and roads in all parts of the colony, the extension of telegraphic communications, the supply of water to the goldfields, and the purchase of native land. The primary intention of the scheme was the development and settling of the North Island to contain any further difficulties which might be experienced from the Maoris; but, in fact, the larger populations of Canterbury and Otago prevailed upon the politicians, and the greater part of the money was spent on the development and extension of South Island roads and railways, bridges, water supply, harbour works and land improvement.

The incentives produced by a growing local market and by the heavy demand from an industrialized Britain directed many graziers to the plough, and, for the first time in many instances, the soils of the burnt and depleted tussock lowlands and gentler foothills were turned and planted in root and grain crops. Between the crop seasons 1872–73 and 1881–82 the acreage of grain expanded from 240,000 to almost 640,000 and that of 'other crops', mainly fodder oats, turnips and rape, from 18,000 to 280,000. In the season 1882–83 production of wheat alone totalled more than 10 million bushels, from almost 400,000 acres. Exports reached a peak of more than 5 million bushels in the following season. The Canterbury–North Otago region contained more than a quarter of the country's settlers and encompassed 57 per cent of all the land in crops, including 75 per cent of the wheat, 65 per cent of the barley and almost half of the oats and of the turnips and rape. In addition, the tussock ranges, plains and downland grazed more than a third of the country's sheep.

This was the era of the bonanza wheat estates, tucked on the leeward side of the Alps in rainshadow country admirably suited to cultivation with its lack of trees, its good drainage and easy slopes. On the larger estates thousands of acres were sown either by hired labour or through leasing part of the holding to contract croppers for rent or for a share in the crop. Land use was extensive and this was made possible by the use of mechanical aids imported at first from England and the United States. The need for machinery gave a fillip in Christchurch and Dunedin to local industries which expanded and diversified in response to the stimulus of the agricultural demand.

But this system of cropping, like the over-zealous burning of the tussock for grazing, was destined for a relatively short life. The primitive mode of growing wheat followed by wheat so long as the land would bear it had, by the early 1880s, brought retribution in the form of declining yields. In the years that followed greater care in crop and pasture management laid the foundations for the future mixed-crop livestock economy of the Canterbury-North Otago region.

In this turbulent and exciting period of development the roles of North and South Island had been completely reversed. Whereas by the 1850s the North Island contained almost two-thirds of the country's 32,000 people and Auckland was the largest urban centre with the Cook Strait settlements running a strong second, thirty years later the balance had been tipped in favour of the South Island. In 1881 New Zealand had a population of 490,000 (exclusive of Maoris), of which the South Island had 62 per cent and the North Island only 38 per cent. Dunedin was the largest city while Christchurch was virtually the same size as Auckland with 35,000 and 36,000 people respectively. Wellington languished with a mere 20,000 residents despite the fact that the capital had been shifted from Auckland in 1865 to a more centralized and accessible position. Dunedin was a commercial and manufacturing city of some note, while Christchurch had been described as the farmers' town. Yet the country was still essentially rural in character, only 38 per cent of the population were living in settlements of more than 1,000 people.

At this time the Maori population – all but less than 2 per cent of it living in the North Island – was still declining in numbers, and great fears were expressed for its total extinction. The Maoris' pattern of distribution was little different from that of the 1850s except that they had retreated or been pushed back even further into the interior. Their numbers in the Waikato, on the Taranaki-Manawatu littoral and along the coastal strip of the Bay of Plenty had been further thinned. The Rotorua-Taupo area, the wild and inaccessible Urewera country and the East Coast, the King country and the Far North were now their strongholds. In the Waikato, a chain of soldier settlements focused on Hamilton and including Te Awamutu, Cambridge and Matamata had been strengthened to contain the tribes to the south in the King country.

In 1870, there were only forty-six miles of railroad in the colony, but by 1881, largely as a result of Vogel's works programmes, 1,287 miles of track were in operation. Of this total, two-thirds were in the South Island and the main trunk line extended for 425 miles from Waipara to Bluff linking the eastern littoral and breaking down the extreme parochialism which had characterized the settlements thirty years previously. Branch lines fingered inland to tap the gold-fields, to bring out the fine Merino wool from the high country stations, the wheat from the plains and downlands, and to distribute the bituminous West Coast coal and foreign goods brought in through the ports at Lyttleton and Port Chalmers.

Meanwhile the rail network in the North Island extended south from Auckland only as far as Te Awamutu, north from Wellington to Masterton, from Foxton to Waverley, from Hawera to New Plymouth and Waitara and from Ormondville to Napier – a useful but disconnected system which had to wait another twenty-seven years before it was opened to through traffic from Auckland to Wellington.

But things had started to move again in the North Island. Once the rebellious Maoris had been cowed and dispirited and large areas of native land confiscated, the scene was set for the wholesale and indiscriminate destruction of the island's mantle of dense forest. Virgin stands of valuable timber which could only be regarded as a nuisance and a 'weed' in the pioneer circumstances were beginning to be assaulted on a grand scale with a calculating eye not for the timber but for the future pastures the land would provide. By 1881 more than 2 million acres had been sown to pasture though not ploughed. The acreage of pasture in the North Island had expanded from 970,000 to 1,715,000 in four years.

The year 1882 was one of prime importance to the economic and national development of the country and in the subsequent shape and character of the landscapes of New Zealand. In that year two shipments of frozen meat, totalling a little under 9,000 carcasses, were landed in London in good condition. In 1883 130,000 carcasses of mutton and a small quantity of beef were shipped. This was the signal for the almost simultaneous erection of freezing works in Dunedin, Christchurch, Wellington, Auckland and Napier. It was the signal which began the era of refrigerated cargoes which linked the large market of Great Britain with the surplus and potential capacity of New Zealand's pastures. Within a decade more than 1·6 million sheep and lambs were exported annually, and there were twenty-one freezing works in the colony, twelve in the North Island and nine in the South Island. Together, these works were capable of killing and freezing up to 4 million sheep per annum. Almost as important were the industries established in association with the large freezing works – tallow works, fellmongeries, meat canning plants, sausage skin factories, oil and manure works. The freezing works had become a characteristic feature of many New Zealand towns, employing hundreds of workers – both casual and permanent – and covering large areas with extensive buildings and holding paddocks for stock awaiting slaughter. Located, of necessity, on rail links for the concentration of livestock and the transhipment of the frozen carcasses to the port, they were busy enterprises, especially in the late spring and summer when the young fat stock was sent forward. Railway yards were full of stock wagons, the holding yards jammed with stock, and a nauseating stench emanated from processing and from the disposal of waste.

With the inauguration of the frozen meat trade, sheep farming in the colony underwent a radical change. Before 1882 wool was the chief consideration, the surplus stock finding its way to the boiling down vats, tallow and hides being the only other products of value. After refrigeration, sheep-raising for mutton became the most profitable branch of farming. Sheep increased greatly in value and all farmers carried flocks of pure and crossbred sheep if conditions of soil, slope, climate and pasture were or could be made appropriate. The Merinos of the South Island and the heavy long-woolled Lincoln and Romney Marsh breeds of the North Island were not ideally suited for the frozen meat trade. Crossbreeding was undertaken – the long-woolled ewes of the North Island were mated with Shropshire, Hampshire and Southdown rams, and the Merinos of the South Island with Lincoln, Leicester and other long-wool breeds. In 1881, the number of sheep in the colony totalled 13 million; by 1893 this figure had risen to 19·4 million. Another technological change assisted the industry. The conversion of sail to steam increased the efficiency and speed of shipment. In the early 1890s there were thirty-six vessels engaged in the New Zealand meat trade of which only six were still under sail.

Although refrigeration gave the sheep industry a great boost and permitted increased diversification of its market products, its greatest influence was in the opportunity it provided for the dairy industry. In 1882 the cooperative dairy industry got under way. As an inducement to the establishment of factories, the government offered a bonus of £500 for the first fifty tons of cheese produced under the factory system. By 1893, fifty-five cheese factories, sixty-two butter factories, sixty creameries and two milk condensing factories had been established. In addition, there were thirty-three new factories under construction. These factories were mainly in the North Island where they were built along the west coast in Taranaki and the Manawatu in particular, in the Waikato valley and in South Auckland. Those few which had been established in the South Island were mainly in Southland and Otago. In 1881 exports of dairy products totalled 5,482 hundredweight; twenty years later the figure had reached 741,561 hundredweight. In the nine years from 1901 to 1910 sheep numbers grew steadily – from 20·2 million to 24 million – but dairy cows increased steeply from 272,000 to 633,000. The greater part of the increase in both sheep and dairy cows was in the North Island. Farming in the South Island experienced little expansion during this period.

Two things made this North Island development possible: legislation designed to encourage land development, and the perfection of the bush-burn technique of land clearance. Reforms in 1892 and 1894 under the Liberal Party prevented further land aggregation and made it possible for the government to purchase alienated land for closer subdivision. Land was now procurable by the smaller settler on very reasonable terms either by purchase or by lease in perpetuity. Whereas the South Island had been developed under a system of extensive estates, the Seddon reforms encouraged the small operator in the North Island and made possible the advent of the 'cow cocky'.

While the land reforms contributed to a much closer settlement pattern in the North Island and, indeed, made some inroads on the giant estates controlled by the 'squattocracy' in the South Island, the most spectacular landscape change was in the removal of the bush cover from the steep, unstable hillsides of the North Island. As in the tussock grazing era, fire was the primary tool in the settler's hands.

The bush burn technique cleared more than 10 million acres of land in New Zealand between 1870 and 1910. It was a technique the rudiments of which were known to the Maoris, but the pioneer settlers incorporated in their methods experience brought from Australia and Canada. Under New Zealand conditions it became a refined, expert and unique procedure. The usual sequence was for the farmer to clear the dense matted undergrowth with his bill hook or 'slasher', and to cut down the smaller trees – those with a diameter of less than about 18 inches. This clearing was normally carried out about June, and the scrub and fern and the smaller trees which had been felled were left to dry until February or March when the match was applied. If the weather was dry and there was a favourable wind on the day of the burn, the fire would sweep through everything, leaving only the blackened and wasted trunks of the larger trees standing as stark sentinels over the tangled mass of smouldering logs and a thick layer of ash. Occasionally the fire would rage unchecked and whole watersheds would be destroyed by the leaping flames. The success of the burn was measured in the number of logs and stumps left lying about. If the burn was only moderately successful their disposal often took the farmers a number of years. Logs were not so difficult to handle as they could be collected together in great piles and refired, but the extraction and disposal of the stumps was a much more difficult task. On steeper country they were often left to rot over the years but on the better country where eventually the farmer planned to plough it was essential to remove them.

Immediately following the fire, grass seed was scattered in the ashes. By the next spring the farmer would have to have a flock of ewes or herd of cattle on the land with fairly heavy stocking ratios to graze and stamp the pastures in order to consolidate the soil and to keep down the native ferns and forest seedlings. The carefully controlled use of grazing as part of the development sequence was a critical element and one which, unless carried out carefully, often resulted in reversion to native vegetation.

While pastures were being established in the ashes, the farmer busied himself 'logging up', splitting posts and rails for his fences, perhaps planting a few acres of turnips or other root crops, or improving the often miserable hut he had first erected on his land. With heavy and well distributed rainfall throughout most of the North Island the tracks and roads to the farm and creamery and to the nearest town were frequently impassable quagmires which isolated the farmer from regular contact with his supplies and market. His instruments were primitive, his task difficult and formidable, his progress remarkable.

But it would be wrong to think that all the indigenous forest cover was destroyed without thought or consequence. Very early in the settler's assault on the bush some people voiced strong concern about its loss and the need to maintain a supply of merchantable timber. The timber industry itself, at the turn of the century, was a reckless consumer of the forest stands, and accounted for a considerable number of the colony's workforce. Even in 1891 there were 243 sawmills operating in the country – 119 in the North Island and 124 in the South Island – employing 3,266 persons. Apart from workers at the mills, men were engaged in the preliminary work of felling, logging, hauling, building dams, laying tramways, and in some cases logs were conveyed to the sawmills by freight train or coastal vessel.

Timber was cut and sawn for local use wherever it was available but, even in the earliest years of their settlement, those areas near Christchurch and Dunedin, which had been less well endowed with original stands, experienced difficulty in maintaining an adequate supply. The Auckland province became the major source of timber supply for the remainder of the colony and for the small trickle of exports. More than 400 million superficial feet of sawn timber were cut annually in the colony, quite apart from that destroyed by fire.

Closely linked to the timber industry were the kauri gum (or kauri resin) diggings of the northern part of the Auckland provincial district, from North Cape to the middle Waikato. Kauri gum had featured on the export lists from the 1850s and in times of commercial recession, when prices for agricultural produce fell, the gum offered a useful backstop for the workers in northern New Zealand. In 1860 the export was only 1,046 tons valued at £9 per ton; in 1893 it amounted to 8,317 tons valued at £61 per ton. In 1893 there were almost 7,000 people employed on the 'gumlands' including 1,244 Maoris. Probing the swamps with their augers and pieces of fencing wire, digging over the wet, heavy podsolized and acidic clay soils and wallowing in muddy, slushy pits and swamps, and living a rough, uncomfortable life in tents and shacks, some diggers found the gum a useful means of accumulating capital, while most eked out an existence in the 'roadless' north where access was for years maintained by coastal vessel and where the rail link from Auckland did not finally reach Whangarei until 1925.

The agricultural expansion of the North Island was especially responsible for the fundamental shift in the distribution of population which followed its subjugation and progress. The pacification of the Maori, refrigeration, generous terms for land acquisition offered to the settler, and the difficulties in obtaining choice land in the South Island attracted the new migrants to the North Island, and drew some of the land hungry from the South. Whereas the period from 1850 until 1881 had been one in which the South Island boomed, the following twenty years and, for that matter, the greater part of the present century, have witnessed the unrestricted progress of the North Island.

This shift in economic emphasis can be most readily traced through the adjustment of the population to the opportunities offering. In 1881 the South Island contained two-thirds of New Zealand's population. Between 1886 and 1891 a quickening in the rate of North Island's expansion could be identified even though it did not gain a numerical advantage over the South Island until 1901. In 1886 the North and South Islands had European populations of 250,482 and 327,592 respectively. By 1891 the North Island had increased its total by 30,973 (12·3 per cent) while the South Island had added only 17,119 people (5·2 per cent). In the 1880s the Maori population plunged to its lowest figure – 38,000 – following which a slow recovery was made. In 1891 the Maoris numbered 41,993.

From 1891 to 1901 the North Island European population increased by more than 100,000 to reach 390,579 and achieve numerical dominance over the South Island which had added 37,000 people in the same period and totalled 382,140 at the century's turn. The following years strengthened the North Island's commanding position. By 1911 it had 55·9 per cent of the country's one million inhabitants.

Auckland had clearly become once more the dominant urban centre and recorded a population of 115,750. Wellington (82,800), Christchurch (87,400) and Dunedin (67,200) were unchallenged as the next largest cities. The secondary urban centres were still very small, only Gisborne, Napier, Wanganui, Palmerston North, Timaru and Invercargill having accumulated more than 10,000 persons each. Hamilton, the regional centre of the rapidly developing and rich Waikato dairy country, had only 5,700 people in 1911. It was not until the advent of the motor vehicle as a common necessity that accessibility improved and the future regional centres were able to grow to a significant size. An almost exact balance between the rural and urban sectors of the population had been achieved by 1911, just over 50 per cent now living in towns of more than 1,000. This figure was a significant change from the conditions prevailing in 1881 when the urban population comprised only 39 per cent of the total. The shift from rural to urban was an indication of the growing diversity of economic activities as the towns became essential links in the processing of agricultural products and in servicing the rural population. As in other western countries, New Zealand was to become a highly urbanized society in the following years as rural electrification and mechanization allowed agriculture to become more efficient and less labour intensive.

The change in the balance of population between the two islands was assisted by the extension and improvement of the communication systems. Towns such as Taumaranui, Ohakune and Taihape, in the interior of the North Island, virtually owed their existence to the rail link which was being pushed through to connect Auckland and Wellington. Each in turn became the centre of construction as the railhead reached them. Then they became an important link in the system as stations, water points for the thirsty steam engines struggling up the steep gradients, and the bases for repair gangs which waged a continuous battle to keep the line free of slips and washouts. The progress of construction was slower in the North Island as bush had to be cleared, deep cuttings excavated, tunnels driven and bridges and viaducts constructed to cross the deep ravines in the hill country. But in the period to 1914, 1,200 miles of hard-won narrow gauge track, difficult and costly to maintain, was laid in the North Island.

The next quarter of a century was a significant one for the rapidly maturing nation, which was granted Dominion status in 1907. Population increased at a favourable rate, World War I united the country, and the government used the rehabilitation scheme for returned servicemen as an opportunity to pursue its policy of encouraging closer rural settlement by subdividing land acquired by the Crown for farms. During the war the state had actively intervened in the marketing of primary produce as an emergency measure. From 1921 onwards, however, the orderly marketing of pastoral products became a distinct part of the government's policy of agricultural development, culminating in the introduction of the 'guaranteed' price which stabilized dairy farm incomes and encouraged the farmer to plan and develop his property on a long-term basis. The great depression affected the whole nation but it had certain beneficial side effects. One such effect was that hundreds of men on relief labour were taken to the Volcanic Plateau, and housed in tents and set to work trudging across otherwise non-productive land planting millions of *Pinus radiata* seedlings soon to form the basis of thousands of acres of exotic forests. Men were also employed to drain the peat swamps of the Waikato and other areas, to raise stopbanks, to stack logs from the peat and to clear and prepare land for farm settlers. In the wake of increased motorized transport, narrow metalled roads were pushed through previously inaccessible and poorly serviced country, bringing closer contact between farm and processing units in the country towns.

By the end of the 1930s, the country was settled and established, its farm landscapes generally neat and tidy arrangements of fences, hedges and shelter belts. The latter were a pleasant mixture of evergreen indigenous and deciduous exotic species. New Zealand's timber-built towns and cities were extensive in area but with clean environments, unsullied by the smoke and grime of industrial areas, and lacking the depressing high density row housing or 'back to back' characteristic of British industrial towns.

The welfare state guarded and guided the rights and lives of its 1·5 million citizens, two-thirds of whom by the mid-1930s lived in urban settlements. In view of the varied relief and the difficulties of establishing a sound agricultural economy distant from markets and in an alien environment, the changes wrought by the immigrant European in less than 100 years could only be described as spectacular.

Part Four
The contemporary scene

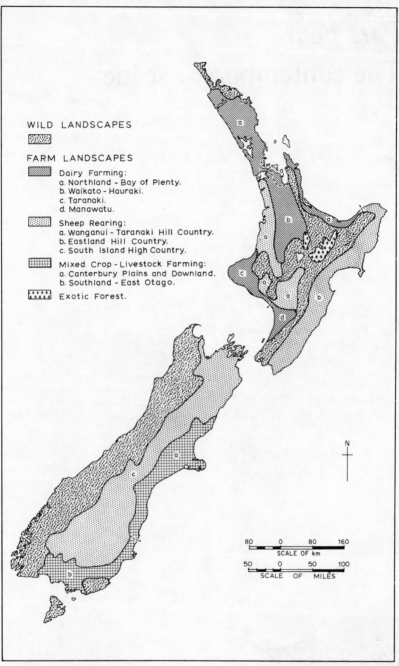

WILD LANDSCAPES

FARM LANDSCAPES

Dairy Farming:
a. Northland - Bay of Plenty.
b. Waikato - Hauraki.
c. Taranaki.
d. Manawatu.

Sheep Rearing:
a. Wanganui - Taranaki Hill Country.
b. Eastland Hill Country.
c. South Island High Country.

Mixed Crop - Livestock Farming:
a. Canterbury Plains and Downland.
b. Southland - East Otago.

Exotic Forest.

N

80   0   80   160
SCALE OF km

50   0   50   100
SCALE OF MILES

5. *Major landscapes*

Chapter 5
The 'wild' landscapes

The adjective 'wild' when applied to countryside, and particularly to the pre-dominantly raw and rugged New Zealand landscape, is a most convenient designation. Wild landscape is an especially apposite shorthand reference to that part of the face of the land which remains unoccupied and least transformed by man, and which retains at least something of its pristine character and appearance. There is, of course, today very little, if any, of New Zealand where the indirect effects of, first, Polynesian, and later, European culture have not effected acute, often brutal but sometimes unpredicted changes. This is despite the fact that human occupancy is of much shorter duration – at least 1,000 but on present evidence probably not more than 1,500 years – than in most other lands. Even a short generation ago the maps of official agencies dismissed much of the inland detail of Fiordland by printing 'unexplored' generously over the sheets. Now, however, the term 'natural landscape' is nowhere strictly applicable except to a purely theoretical pre-human reconstruction. The wild landscape, the untamed and unsubdued countryside, the unoccupied land, the back-country: these are terms much to be preferred to 'natural landscape' or to the use of adjectives like 'untouched', 'untransformed', or 'virgin'. They are to be preferred on both popular and scientific grounds.

The wild back-country and high-country landscapes of New Zealand are extensive and widespread. They embrace probably 22 million acres – not less than one-third of the superficial area of the North Island, South Island, Stewart Island and the 'offshore islands' combined. With its severely dismembered and contorted surface, its steep slopes, its difficulty of access, and with a mere 2·78 million people concentrated in a small sector of its 66 million acres, it is little wonder that New Zealand has large tracts of unoccupied land, their scenery apparently little disturbed by direct interference at the hand of man – Maori or *pakeha*, past or present. Yet, significantly, man has indirectly had subtle and serious effect, if visually not readily detectable, on these wild tracts of remote and inaccessible countryside. Today they present New Zealanders with re-serves of land and scenery and with economic potentials as well as with prob-lems that are tricky, involved and of increasing concern.

It is to the wild and untamed countryside that one must go to experience, to understand, and to wonder at the difficulties that once confronted moahunter and Maori tribes (as well as their European pioneering successors) where, after perilous and accidental voyages over thousands of landless miles, they encountered near-impossible problems of penetration. Complexity of slope, relief and drainage, the awesome density, strangeness and tangle of vegetation, the prolonged and heavy rain, the penetrating humidity, the chill and hush and silence, the loneliness and isolation are to this day essential traits of the wild and remoter countryside. Indeed in this age of urbanization, noise, traffic and of affluent domestic holidaymakers and foreign tourists, much of this constitutes a major part of the unoccupied back-country's appeal. It is a new-found, as yet little exploited resource, a potential asset that, if and when it is 'improved' and 'developed', runs the risk of having part of its unique attraction rapidly diminished, if not destroyed. The provision of access, especially for prospective large numbers of tourists, is not likely to be conducive to the preservation of the delight that many folk find in the silence, loneliness and awe of the wild and 'natural'.

Here is a problem of widespread contemporary concern in New Zealand. There is at present increasingly bitter debate and prolonged political indecision as to whether, in general or in specific instances and localities, to preserve intact and inviolate what is popularly imagined to be the residue of the pre-human scene with its 'indigenous' flora and fauna and undisrupted 'natural' environment; or whether to 'conserve' it by allowing carefully controlled access, severely restricted use of its water and mineral resources, and the development of its unique scenic and scientific attractions but subject to prescribed rules, regulations and restraints.

New Zealand's wild landscapes occur in most parts of the country. For obvious reasons they occupy larger areas in the rugged and more thinly peopled South Island. They embrace a great variety of contrasting locations and habitats. There are elongated, but fractured, and much dissected stretches of elevated alpine ice, rock and scree above the occupied South Island 'high country', remote vertically walled saltwater fiords in the far south, volcanic cones in the North Island with concentric altitudinal rings of vegetation – smooth and symmetrical from a safe distance, gashed and precipitous and tangled with scrub or treacherous with ice and snow on close contact – densely forested mountain massifs in Nelson, and narrow ridges of forested ranges reaching from the fringe of suburban Wellington to East Cape. There are also expansive plateau wildernesses of scrub and tussock in the North Island interior; little, warm, forested subtropical islands, hitherto preserved as scenic reserves or bird sanctuaries and unvisited except by permit rarely sought and still more rarely granted; protected, northern relics of lordly kauri forest; and in many places wild stretches of wind-lashed coast with little frequented beaches interrupted by dark and brooding headlands.

While most of the unoccupied countryside is mountainous and indeed comprises lofty alpine terrain, the designation wild landscape includes also long,

6. *Ninety Mile Beach: Northland*
The wide crescent of beach extends for 60 (not 90) miles unbroken and unoccupied along the western side of the northernmost peninsula, where it forms an alternative motor highway. It is representative of many stretches of wild coastland, sandy and rocky, smooth and rough, throughout the country.

exposed and hitherto unoccupied littorals of dune sand, lowland swamps (though most of these have now been converted for occupation and farm production) and elevated ash-strewn plateau. Not only difficult terrain distant from the initial points of European settlement, but also less fertile, windswept lowland and coastal areas and inaccessible offshore islands especially off the eastern seaboard of the North Island from the Bay of Plenty to the Bay of Islands comprise part of the still untamed, unordered, little used countryside. In terms of modern transport they are never distant from centres of population. Indeed, a postwar motorized urban community is discovering their attractions, and beginning to utilize many hitherto wild and little known parts of the country and, in the process, is reducing their wildness, inaccessibility and lack of occupancy. With the establishment of amphibious air services and the construction of new tourist roads, city dwellers are increasingly impinging on the solitude of what hitherto have been the unvisited and exclusive domain of solitary musterers, or of opossum trappers, pig hunters, deer cullers like Crump's 'good, keen man', scientists and elderly *pakeha* recluses, or still-tattooed Maori elders.

With the unoccupied land, the New Zealander associates above all the 'bush', the visually dull and sombre native forest and its reduced remnant of an indigenously rich and varied avifauna. Only the South Islander may think first of a sparse subalpine vegetation of lofty wildernesses of grey rock and glaring snow, or of the expanses of tussock-clad greywacke mountain slope with occasional green-black 'hangers' of southern beech and a numerous population of exotic ungulates – moose, deer, wapiti, thar and chamois. Rarely is the 'bush' preserved today in its pristine grandeur. Much of the forest cover of the wild landscape has at some stage or other been cut over and mutilated by the extraction of timber – kauri, rimu, totara and matai. Although vigorous growth has subsequently obliterated many of the raw signs of interference, mature forest giants, which take centuries to reach massive proportions, are lacking. Elsewhere, in advance of the extraction of timber, exotic animal pests, notably red deer and more recently the Australian opossum, have wrought extensive damage in the forest, just as on the tussock lands rabbits in their scores of millions were often the principal agents in modifying the floristic composition of the grassland and in exposing the thin and tenuous soils until the 'killer policy' of rabbit boards virtually eliminated this menace a generation ago. In the cut-over forests, too, wild pigs and feral cattle, horses and goats as well as deer and opossums often prevent or retard the vigorous regeneration that a forest climate would generously allow. The remaining forest wildernesses are often so isolated, on such steep slopes, or in such elevated, exposed and edaphic-ally unusual sites as to be quite unrepresentative of the indigenous New Zealand bush. Today they are conserved as watershed protection forest and as regulators of run-off in catchments where water is increasingly important for electricity generation or urban domestic supply, and not as potential sources of indigenous timber, nor primarily for their scientific interest or tourist appeal. Fortunately a mature stand of kauri trees has been preserved at Waipoua in Northland, where otherwise only very small patches of kauri or single trees of massive girth are extant.

In the elevated tussock and subalpine terrain of Marlborough, Canterbury and Otago, where the indigenous vegetation was sparse, discontinuous, necessarily hardy and remarkably adapted to rigorous environmental conditions, changes in the appearance of the landscape are less obvious and more difficult to determine. The treading and picking by Merino sheep of unfenced summer range as well as the depredations of deer and rabbits, and damage caused by the runholders' repeated burning wherever the cover was sufficient to carry a fire, have brought subtle changes. The snowtussock has often disappeared. Sheltered hangers of southern beech have been reduced in acreage and their undergrowth destroyed. Finer adjustments have been made as fire resistant and unpalatable subalpine species have persisted at the expense of others intolerant of fire, unresistant to grazing and not adapted to the effects of alien and immigrant invaders. But most obvious, once its man-induced origins were suspected and demonstrated, has been the speeded disintegration of the greywacke bedrock and the exposure of bare schist surfaces. Perched talus has surged downslope invading the bunched grassland with swollen tongues of scree, made available by elevated exposure of jointed bedrock to frost and wind. After heavy rain it has often been carried thousands of feet down steep mountain sides while deep gutters and gullies have been eroded into the stabilized and partly vegetated mantle of shingle on valley walls. Gravel fans at the base of slopes have grown and changed their shape, and the load of grey-white shingle on the wide floor of U-shaped valleys has swollen at an unaccustomed rate presenting an impossible burden to the jade-coloured braids of rivers now derived from diminished glacier sources. Elsewhere, on alpine slopes and the gravel floors of intermontane basins alike, parched and scorching föhn winds have helped to remove thin, immature, yellow soils and to expose bedrock and gravel – a process first initiated by fire and grazing. The manmade deserts of Central Otago, the Mackenzie country and the Awatere valley (in Marlborough) are the outcome.

In the absence of mineral resources and the impossibility of its use even for the most extensive pastoral purposes, much of the New Zealand wilderness has remained Crown land. Some is still held by Maoris under customary tenure or as 'Maori freehold'. Large areas are administered today as national parks. In addition to ten national parks totalling in excess of 5 million acres in area there are 1 million acres designated as scenic reserves, historic reserves or bird sanctuaries. Almost 10 million acres more are classed and administered as state forest, much of which is untended protection forest and little of which has any significance as a future source of indigenous timber. A further 6·5 million acres of unoccupied Crown and Maori land is classed as 'waste land such as mountain tops, bare rock, water surfaces etc.'. Some of this is capable of development dependent upon accessibility and contour; and indeed more than a million acres is in the process of development as farmland by the Department of Lands and Survey.

New Zealand has preserved land for public use and as pleasances since its infant colonial days. Small areas of reserves, domains and public lands were set aside from the beginnings of organized settlement. The first national park was established in 1887 when the three mountain peaks in the interior of the North Island – Ruapehu (9,175 feet), Ngauruhoe and Tongariro, centres of continued volcanic activity, of potential winter sport and ski-grounds as well as of particular botanical interest – were gifted to the nation by Te Heuheu Tukino and other Tuwharetoa chiefs. Special legislation established the Egmont National Park in 1900. Legislation for the establishment and administration of future national parks came in 1928. Under it the alpine park of Arthur's Pass and the Abel Tasman Park in Tasman Bay, Nelson were set aside in 1929 and 1942. But under postwar legislation, the basis was laid for an integrated network of national parks, to be uniformly administered under the Minister of Lands by a National Parks Authority and a series of National Parks Boards. Since the coming into operation of the 1952 Act, the Fiordland, Mount Cook, Urewera, Nelson Lakes, Westland and Mount Aspiring National Parks have been established.

The 5 million acres in national parks, almost 8 per cent of the total area of New Zealand, comprise a large and representative portion of the country's wild landscapes.

Tongariro's 162,000 acres – roughly half-way between Auckland and Wellington urban clusters of population – are the most frequented. The three giant volcanic cones, sporadically or continuously active, rise above the western rim of the Volcanic Plateau overlooking the blue circle of Lake Taupo, the stark Rangipo 'desert' of scrub and red tussock between the park and the Kaimanawas, as well as the forested semicircle of confusingly dissected hill country to the west. In most places silver beech and scrub species climb to the snowline. Beyond, in winter, crisp snow smooths the gashed dark surface of recent lava flows and reaches to the rim of Ruapehu's steaming crater lake. Since 1950 access to Tongariro National Park has been greatly improved, and amenities so intensively developed that on sunny August weekends as many as 10,000 people may visit the snowfields. Ski tows and chair lifts take skiers to 7,350 feet. Above the luxury tourist hotel, Chateau Tongariro, with its golf course, tennis courts and bowling greens, are log cabins, motor camps, camp sites and caravan bays and the alpine village of Mount Ruapehu; and on the mountain slopes tramping, mountain and ski clubs have provided for the younger and more

7. *Tongariro National Park*

The volcanic piles of Ruapehu (foreground) with Tongariro and Ngauruhoe beyond it, overlook the Volcanic Plateau to the northeast. This wild landscape forms a vast winter playground for increasing thousands of New Zealanders. The snow cover is much more extensive in mid-winter.

adventurous visitors a growing number of mountain lodges, huddled against the snow.

Mount Egmont's symmetrical but isolated cone is ringed by a lowland of intensive dairy farming on New Zealand's most evergreen pastures. It provides an elevated park of 82,000 acres, its vegetation changing from dense forest of rimu, rata and totara to kamahi and mountain cedar (but no beech), alpine shrubs and almost bare rock in regular concentric altitudinal zones. In addition to the provision of roads, tracks, huts and ski tows, the Egmont Park Board faces the problem of destroying feral goats, which browse on seedlings and the forest understorey, and fast increasing numbers of opossums, which feed on the foliage of even the tallest trees. The Egmont National Park is a readily accessible playground. The care and conservation of its vegetative cover is of both aesthetic and economic interest. The dense radial pattern of streams from its slopes spread out over one of the North Island's most productive and intensively occupied pastoral regions.

The North Island's third and largest national park – almost half a million acres of little modified forest in the Urewera country – is more isolated, less frequented and little known, although the Rotorua-Wairoa road traverses the park on its tortuous up-and-down crossing of the Huiarau and subsidiary parallel axial ranges and skirts the shore of Lake Waikaremoana. The gently rippling, sheltered waters of the lake are dammed back and held in place by a giant, earthquake-induced earth slump. Although it has only one-tenth of the surface area of Lake Taupo, Waikaremoana stores almost as many acre-feet of water. With its hotel, motor camp, camp site, picnic spots, boating facilities and landings, the lake is the focus of the park. From its elevated blue surface – often thick with paradise, grey, blue and shoveller ducks – and its indented forested shores, dark bush tracks lead into the damp shade of the forest which still shelters a surprisingly large variety of often now rare indigenous bush birds – kakas, parakeets and pigeons. Much of the forest wilderness of the park, including areas of dense virgin bush and giant timber trees, remains inaccessible. Here, in villages in deep mist-shrouded valleys, Maori communities of the Tuhoe tribe lived in isolation. They preserved their traditional pattern of life until the development of Waikaremoana's water power and the Urewera's fine timber, and the economic exploitation of the Volcanic Plateau's exotic timber stands and the improvement of its roads brought sharper culture contact and caused retarded disruption of village life by taking the young people off to work in distant towns and industries.

The South Island has the country's only two coastal parks: the largest in the country (Fiordland, with more than 3 million acres) and the smallest (Tasman, 43,474 acres). The Abel Tasman National Park between Tasman Bay and Golden Bay, Nelson, extends inland from precipitous cliffs and from coves with unspoiled beaches of dark golden sand a distance of six miles to mountain forests of red beech. From the lower slopes, up to 1,000 feet, a mixed forest has been stripped in an attempt to farm the land. Some however remains; elsewhere scrub represents an early stage of forest regeneration. The park has no permanent accommodation, but holiday flats are available at the old homestead at Totaranui, and shelter for marooned fishing parties at Mutton Cove. Coastal camp sites are a major attraction. The park is appropriately named after the Dutch navigator who in 1642 anchored offshore here in Tasman Bay in the lee of the Tata Islands. Unfortunately his visit, in sharp contrast with that of contemporary visitors seeking sun and surf or bush solitude, was so marred by the tragic first encounter of European and Maori that Tasman gave the name Murderers Bay to the sunny, mild and sheltered arm of the sea which the park overlooks. Today, however, it bears his own name.

Fiordland is one of the world's largest national parks, 3 million acres of wilderness, all of it of striking relief and geomorphology. Of all parts of the country it is the one most remote from those in which most New Zealanders live. Except for the road up the Eglinton valley and through the Homer tunnel to Milford Sound and the road recently bulldozed through dense forest on precipitous slopes from the West Arm of Lake Manapouri over the Wilmot Pass to Deep Cove, Doubtful Sound, the only practicable way of reaching the fiords of the remote southwest coast of the South Island is by sea or by amphibian aircraft.

Yet in the earliest days of European contact with New Zealand, Fiordland was one of the better known and most frequented parts of the newfound land. After James Cook's precise investigation and charting of the coast of Fiordland, 'Dusky Bay' became one of the most often visited parts of the New Zealand coastline. It had French, English, Spanish and Australian visitors from thirty to fifty years before Europeans first entered the Manukau at Auckland or Port Nicholson at Wellington. The vertically walled fiords provided shelter from storm and wind. Their waters were so deep that anchorage was, according to Cook, possible only 'in coves . . . very near the shore' where, however, places for tying up were 'numerous . . . safe and commodious'. In Pickersgill Harbour – on the south shore of Dusky Sound between Indian Island (so-named because Cook's men saw there a Polynesian) and Cascade Cove – Cook moored his barque in deep water (17 fathoms) with trees overhanging the gunwale. But there were features of Fiordland which even Cook was not happy about. Between the rock-walled gashes cut by ice to a depth of more than 1,000 feet below sea level, the even-topped remnant surfaces of the ancient block of grey and dark-green gneisses rise to over 7,000 feet in the north and to more than 4,000 feet approaching Foveaux Strait. Cook dismissed this mountain interior as 'barren and naked'; and to him the southernmost part of the South Island presented generally 'a prospect rude and craggy', with 'almost continual rain' and myriads of small black sandflies. Nevertheless, with its deep, sheltered waters and bush to the shoreline, with its wealth of fish, wild fowl and seals, abundant fresh water and ample 'tea-tree' and rimu for concocting an antiscorbutic 'spruce beer', it was an attractive revictualling place for early explorers and the source of rich harvests for the sealers who later decimated its coastal wildlife. Such attractions gave Fiordland a European history as old, strange and exciting as any part of the country. Yet, before European settlement was organized in New Zealand, Fiordland was virtually abandoned for more than a century to the sole occupance of sandflies and other forms of native life and to the deer, wapiti and moose that Europeans brought.

Structurally, geologically and geomorphologically, Fiordland is sharply marked off from the rest of the country. It is a structural mountain massif of Ordovician and Cambrian schists, marble, quartzite and paragneiss, and of diorite gneiss of doubtful early Palaeozoic Age. Its landward structural edge is marked by the long axes of a series of deep, glaciated 'cold-water' lakes – Te Anau, Manapouri, Monowai, Hauroko and Poteriteri – running almost from Milford Sound to Te Waewae Bay on Foveaux Strait.

Quaternary glaciation has cut U-shaped canyons many thousands of feet into the gneiss, dissecting the massif into separate mountain blocks. Westward-moving tongues of ice working along a series of structural faults excavated a radial pattern of overdeepened valleys subsequently invaded by the sea. Equally deep canyons were cut by glaciers on the landward side of the massif. These have been filled behind dams of glacial debris by freshwater lakes whose floors are sometimes 1,000 feet below sea level and whose waters are 1,500 feet deep. Above the fiords and lakes and their irregularly rectangular pattern of 'arms', are perched lakes and tarns, lofty hanging valleys and elevated cirque basins, some occupied by diminutive glaciers. Over the wet and glistening and almost vertical valley sides tumble cascades of water, threads of white against the mass of dark rock.

So steep are the sheer rock walls of the fiords and higher valleys that they often have no soil or vegetation apart from a mossy, rain-soaked coat of many pastel shades. But on the valley floors, on the shores of lake and fiord, on the islands that frequently interrupt the continuity of water, and over the short but difficult divides between the heads of adjacent valleys, is dense and dripping bush, predominantly of southern beech but including mixed rainforest species. On the easier slopes, above the canyon walls and the tree line at 3,200 feet, are open areas of subalpine shrubs and some grassland. With rainfall totalling in excess of 200 inches every year, there is water everywhere – in lakes and tarns and waterfalls, in tumbling streams, rivers and burns, under foot, in the dripping vegetation, on boggy flats and in the thin but saturated soils. Yet many a day is bright and sunny with sparkling clean air and extremely high visibility. East of the massif still air and sharp frosts are frequent.

Deer and wapiti offer good hunting. The culling of red and fallow deer has been a principal activity of much of Fiordland's only semipermanent population, its professional deer stalkers. Streams and lakes provide excellent fishing for brown and rainbow trout and Atlantic salmon. Perhaps the most interesting biological fact about Fiordland, however, concerns the *takahe*. This flightless bird, *Notornis mantelli*, was long thought to be extinct until in 1948 it was rediscovered. This remarkable event took place on the open tussocky expanses of the Murchison range between the Middle and South Fiords of Lake Te Anau. The birds are few and rigorously protected. Attempts have been made to rear them in captivity in the North Island and entry to the Murchison mountain area on the western shore of Lake Te Anau is forbidden except along the lowest 500 yards of the fishing rivers which flow from the reserve into the lake and its 'arms'.

The national park is increasingly attractive to visitors in other ways. Amphibian aircraft have ample landings since the smooth waters of lakes and fiords occupy so much of the region's surface. Launches ply the inland waterways. In addition to the road which skirts Manapouri and Te Anau on its way to the Eglinton and Hollyford valleys and the shattered rocky portals of the Homer tunnel which provides access to the majestic scenery of Milford Sound, tracks have been cut from lakeside landings through the rainforest to the mountain passes leading to Doubtful, Dusky, George and Milford Sounds. Most famous of these is the Milford Track and its three-day 'finest walk in the world' from Glade House at the head of Lake Te Anau over the McKinnon pass, past the 1,904 feet high Sutherland falls and steeply down the Arthur valley alongside Lake Ada to Milford Sound.

Huts, built originally to shelter government deer stalkers, are numerous. There are motor camps at Te Anau, Milford and Cascade Creek. Accommodation is available at Manapouri and at Doubtful Sound, and tourist hotels at Te Anau and at Milford Sound.

Fiordland's tourist resources are already of considerable importance and of very much greater potential. Its only other resource is its developed and potential water power. The development of the two – tourist and water power resources – have already been in conflict and the subject of public controversy. With the large-scale development of the major accessible hydroelectric power resources in other parts of New Zealand – notably on the Waikato, Waitaki and Clutha rivers – the vast potential of power available in Fiordland is attracting increasing attention. With its natural lake storage and fast descending rivers regularly furnished with abundant run-off from heavy rain, Fiordland, despite its isolation, must produce an increasing share of the energy required by an expanding economy. The small hydro station at Monowai has generated electricity for forty years. Now New Zealand's largest power station with an ultimate capacity of between 600,000 and 1,000,000 kW is under construction in Fiordland.

The project is estimated to cost $250 million. This undertaking has already brought to Fiordland, as construction workers and temporary residents, a greater population than this remote part of the country has seen since sealing gangs of hundreds from New South Wales lived there a century and a half ago. The feverish activity of earthmoving machines, trucks, blasting equipment and tunnelling gear have brought raucous and unaccustomed noise and disturbance to a region long characterized by quiet and a minimum of evidence of human disturbance.

The 'Manapouri scheme' has also occupied thousands of column-inches in the New Zealand press in recent years. Despite the misgivings and vociferous arguments of conservationists, the government is pushing ahead with the plan.

The project involves the damming of the Waiau river outlet of Lake Manapouri to raise its level and storage capacity. The rapids which connect Lakes Te Anau and Manapouri will be eliminated and the two lakes will become virtually one. Fortunately the lake shores are for the most part steep, but even so, a large acreage of forest will be submerged, though the government has undertaken to fell the trees below the new shore line so that a ghostly grey dead forest of trunks and boles will not for decades continue to interrupt the surface of the enlarged lake. The flow of water from the lake will be diverted from the east coast to the west. After being plunged 750 feet down a vertical shaft to a subterranean powerhouse being built in a vast dripping chamber excavated in the metamorphic rock, it will be discharged through a six-mile-long tunnel into Deep Cove at the head of the Malaspina arm of Doubtful Sound. A road has been cut over Wilmot Pass; and the construction workers at the western end are being housed at Deep Cove during construction in the *Wanganella*, a passenger vessel which for many years carried thousands of Australians and New Zealanders – and others – back and forth across the Tasman Sea.

An option on Manapouri's enormous supply of cheap power, available for distribution by 1970, has been granted to Comalco, a combine in which Con-zinc Riotinto of Australia Ltd is associated with the Kaiser Corporation of America and with Japanese industrialists. The combine is to use the power to treat 250,000 tons a year of alumina (brought from Weipa, Queensland) at a smelter to be erected at the Bluff where a new town of 20,000 people is envisaged. The 'Manapouri scheme' may be only the first of its kind, for Fiordland is by far the largest source of potential hydro-power remaining in New Zealand.

The South Island's remaining national parks are confined to the mountain axis. They are virtually reserves of alpine terrain, though of completely different character from each other. The Nelson Lakes Park is increasingly accessible and popular as a family resort and recreational area. Only sixty miles from both Nelson and Blenheim, it centres on Lakes Rotoiti (2,000 feet above sea level) and Rotoroa which are set amidst the little disturbed beech forest on the lower slopes of the St Arnaud and Travers ranges and the Spencer mountains. Within easy reach of the growing settlement of St Arnaud near the shore of Rotoiti are facilities for camping, boating, swimming, tramping, mountain climbing, fishing and skiing (by road to Paddy's Hut 3,000 feet up the face of Mount Robert thence by foot track and ski tow to the snowfields). In summer the blue waters of Rotoiti, enclosed and sheltered by the green-black bush-clad slopes of the valleys' ice-cut walls, are increasingly alive with the activities of watersport enthusiasts and ever more frequently dappled with the flash and colour of sail. Arthur's Pass is the only national park served by railway. The citizens of Christchurch, less than 100 miles away, can journey to Arthur's Pass by excursion trains and by ordinary rail services on the Midland Line which, since the opening of the Otira tunnel early in the century, has linked east and west coasts of the South Island, or they can travel by car on the main transalpine highway to Arthur's Pass village.

The park straddles the Southern Alps and sits astride the divide where the pass between the Bealey tributary of the Waimakariri river and the Otira gorge, which leads steeply down to Westland, provides the most important link across the alpine highland of the South Island. Overlooking the settlement with its trampers' huts, chalets, baches, youth hostel, park museum, chapel, railway station and park headquarters are the towering, ice crumbled, rock pinnacles of Avalanche Peak and Mount Aicken, both 6,000 feet; and beyond is the majestic summit of Mount Rolleston (7,453 feet) cradling several diminutive glacier remnants. Directly across the pass from Mount Rolleston is Mount Temple and the cirque of Temple Basin. Here are ski club, university and Park Board huts on what is one of the most used ski grounds in the South Island and virtually on the main divide.

For the rest, the park is an attractive and representative section of the dissected Canterbury high country with glaciated valleys, shingle flats, symmetrical gravel fans, thick beech forest and tussock flats. Along its southern margin flow the milky-green waters of the Waimakariri in a thousand braided ever-changing channels of bleached white shingle. The Poulter, Andrews, Hawdon and Bealey valleys, its left bank tributaries, beyond the limits of the grazier's penetration and his fires, preserve their beech forest to a height of more than 4,000 feet, beyond which is a botanist's paradise of subalpine vegetation – snowgrass, prostrate shrubs, cushion and mat plants, mountain daisies (*Celmesia*), giant mountain buttercups (*Ranunculus lyallii*) and rock species. Unfortunately here too (as well as in the forest) are deer, chamois, thar and opossums. The park's attraction for the botanist and naturalist is enhanced by the contrasts east and west of the divide. With the sharp increase in rainfall west of the divide (Otira has 201 inches of rain a year), the forest is dense and mixed, with rata blossoming on the valley sides, and rimu, kamahi and kahikatea thick and tall on the valley floors. When a moist and maritime westerly air stream flows over the South Island the Otira valley and gorge are choked with ragged nimbus clouds and thrashed with heavy rain. At Arthur's Pass periodic showers or light rain falls, but in the distance to the east clearer skies and a brighter light herald the lack of rain, strong föhn winds and the continuing parched conditions experienced on the open tussock land of the sheep stations at Grasmere and Mount White.

Most famous of New Zealand national parks is Mount Cook, dominated and characterized by the tent-shaped, ice-sheathed mass of the mountain (12,349 feet) which the Maori called the 'cloud piercer'. The park embraces the country's most impressive alpine scenery – 173,000 acres of ice and snow and rock – extending forty miles northeast-southwest along the watershed of the Southern Alps and never more than ten miles from the fretted and frozen roof-top of New Zealand. The main divide of the Southern Alps to the west – the source of most of the glacier ice – is only in two places less than a mile and a half high, and a score of sharp glistening peaks of more than 10,000 feet man this lofty rampart. From its high basins tumble the accumulations of ice which form the Mueller and Hooker glaciers, both within walking distance of the Hermitage, focus of the park. East and north from the Mount Cook range to Élie de Beaumont on the main divide the elevated ice reservoirs supply the eighteen-mile long Tasman glacier, itself 700 feet thick near the Ball Hut, 7,000 feet below the towering adjacent sources of its renewal. East of the Tasman glacier the Malte Brun range has much reduced precipitation and small icefields. Between it and the Liebig range, with only sparse and diminutive glaciers, is the Murchison glacier fed largely from the main divide at its head. Its snout lies more than five miles above its former junction with the Tasman glacier. In the park's northeasternmost corner, the Godley glacier and its tributaries from the main divide and Mount d'Archiac fill the head of the Godley valley which, like the straight, spur-truncated, moraine-flanked valley of the Tasman below the Hermitage, is drained to the lakes of the Mackenzie country with its open, exposed sweep of shallow shingle terraces and its deteriorated tawny tussock grazing land.

When Europeans first saw the magnificent scenery of the Mount Cook region from close quarters, the valley floors (where not occupied by ice) and the lower mountain slopes probably had a vegetation of tall tussock grasses and silver beech for here, close to the divide, rainfall averages more than 150 inches. Above the forest the early explorers, mountaineers and graziers encountered an impenetrably luxurious shrubland. But much of the primeval vegetation both above and below the treeline had already been altered by fire and grazing before the original reserves were set aside in 1885. Although deer are not numerous within the park, thar and chamois have done much damage to the remaining shrubland and subalpine vegetation since their introduction and liberation in the alpine park in 1904 and 1907 respectively. Today forest trees remain only in small patches on the slopes close to the Hermitage in the Hooker valley.

The Hermitage – the third hostelry of that name built to accommodate visitors to this alpine playground – nestles safely on a terrace of small area surrounded by broken stands of beech trees with magnificent views of Mount Cook and Mount Sefton. Here, too, are park headquarters (now responsible for guiding, conducted tours, and all phases of park activity formerly administered from the tourist hotel), as well as post office, garages, store, power house and other services. Across Glencoe Stream and on the coarse gravel flat beneath Governor's Bush there are now motels and youth hostel facilities as well as camping and caravan sites. With the promised growth of New Zealand's tourist traffic, it is not difficult to imagine the mushrooming of a thriving village or small town in this vicinity with the park headquarters as the centre for outfitting and equipping the more adventurous skiers and alpine climbers and also organizing walks, more rigorous tramps, and bus tours for other visitors. Alongside, the airstrip could become one of the busiest in the country for small aircraft.

The Mount Cook park saw the birth of skiing in New Zealand; and for some years Ball glacier was the venue of the national championships. Now there are short tows above and below the Ball Hut. But the skiing area to which they give access is small, the run short and the slope gentle. It is indeed a paradox that here at Mount Cook, with a greater extent of snowfields and of magnificent skiing potential than anywhere else outside the Himalayas and the Antarctic, difficulty of access has put unsurpassed high-speed, long-distance, downhill and giant slalom courses beyond the reach of other than alpine climbers. At present expensive chair lifts or cable cars would be uneconomic as well as impracticable. But the ski plane offers much improved prospects. Already aircraft fitted with skis regularly land parties on the extensive white wildernesses of the upper snowfields of the Tasman, Murchison, Mueller and other glaciers and have made ski mountaineering and ski touring on the glistening roof of New Zealand unique tourist attractions.

Sharing the main divide as a common boundary with the Mount Cook National Park are the 210,000 acres of the Westland National Park. It tumbles precipitously, like its glaciers, from the same lofty peaks down to the Tasman Sea. Here the Fox and Franz Josef glaciers and many smaller ones are fed from the country's most extensive fields of ice and snow, themselves exposed to the moisture-laden air masses off the Tasman Sea. The Fox and Franz Josef tumble abruptly in eight miles or so across the giant alpine fault from in excess of 11,000 feet to within 700 feet of sea level, narrowing as they descend. They have their narrow and retreating snouts, which are visited by so many tourists, tucked away in over-enlarged valleys amidst a rainforest vegetation with subtropical physiognomy. This is the unique attraction of the remote wild landscape of Westland.

The entire coast of Westland has few people and scant settlement. Most settlements derive from earlier periods of extractive economies, based first on gold and later on timber and coal. The gold-mining towns are today either ghostly remnants or have virtually disappeared. But the opening in 1965 of the Haast Pass road, providing a connection across the mountain barrier to Lakes Wanaka and Hawea and to Central Otago, has expanded tourist and holiday interest in South Westland. No longer is it necessary for visitors to the glaciers to double back by the same route: now they can travel through, taking in visits also to the Mount Aspiring and Fiordland National Parks.

The coastal strip is an extensive, elongated waste heap of glacial material dumped by the numerous glaciers that formerly reached the ocean. Across it subsequent torrents have cut wide terraced valleys and floored them with grey-wacke shingle. The road climbs and falls, in a canyon of dark, cool rainforest of rimu, kahikatea and a fringing vegetation of tree and ground ferns, across the hills of glacial debris, emerging occasionally on to open, terraced flats, or passing placid, bush-fringed lakes. The settlements of both the Fox and Franz Josef have tourist hotels, modern motels and camping facilities. Both have airstrips, access to glaciers for the walker and to superb icefields for the alpine climber, to forest scenery and to treelined lakes with the mountain peaks reflected in their still surfaces. This is at once a charming, frighteningly impressive and often unique portion of the New Zealand wilderness, and contributes much to the variety of landscape and scene included in the 5 million acres of New Zealand countryside designated as national parks.

The wild landscape of New Zealand has yet other aspects. There are, for example, large areas of formerly forested hill country in the North Island in Maori or private ownership which have reverted to scrub and second growth. Those to which the Taupo-Napier road gives access, or those in the upper Wanganui valley, are good examples. Here deep dissection has provided a tangle of razorback ridges, steep and slumping valley sides and narrow papa gorges. This is rough and wild country, little of it ever successfully won for farming. It is strange, deranged and riotous country with forest relicts, thick scrub, tall manuka and forest second growth, with clearings of bracken fern or grass. 'Pig country' is the New Zealand designation. It lacks tourist appeal. It can be scenically dull and unexciting. But for the real New Zealander with a yen for the backblocks and for 'roughing it' it offers good sport with abundant deer, pigs and wild goats and the occasional wild bull or brumby.

There are also exquisite island sanctuaries which, because of prohibitions designed to ensure an absolute minimum of human penetration or interference, are known to few New Zealanders except through television documentaries. Such is Coppermine Island, subject of recent disputation. Such are the Three Kings, Little Barrier, Mayor Island, the volcanically active White Island, Kapiti with its variegated bird life, and such is virtually and through its isolation much of Stewart Island. Such, too, are the stormy subantarctic islands – Campbell, Snares, Solander, Bounty, Antipodes and Auckland.

Coppermine Island – to take one example – is the easternmost of a cluster of rocky islets constituting the Marotiri islands in the Hen and Chicken group off Bream Head in Northland and distant nine or ten miles from the peninsular mainland. Few New Zealanders had heard of Coppermine Island until 1965 when this easternmost 'chick' burst into the news and became the subject of heated debate and controversy. To most people the Hen and Chicken group are picturesque offshore islands, one large like a hen with a brood of chickens in close attendance. From the main road through the Northland peninsula they appear to rise steeply in black silhouette from the blue sea. They are a declared wildlife sanctuary and known at close quarters only to yachtsmen, to government officials and to wildlife scientists with permits to set foot, when the state of the sea allows, on their cliffed shores.

But in 1965 a subsidiary of Conzinc Riotinto of Australia Ltd announced its interest in Coppermine Island and subsequently officially applied to the Warden's Court in Auckland for rights to prospect and mine on Coppermine and its neighbouring 'chick' – Whatupuke. Meanwhile a geological report prepared for the government suggests that low grade ores occur in the sedimentary rocks (greywackes) at the western end of Coppermine and on adjacent parts of Whatupuke but with a copper content of only 0·5 per cent. It is estimated that there are no more than 150,000 tons of copper, less than Australia's annual production and only 3 per cent of world output in 1966.

Although it had Maori settlers as late as the 1880s and there have in places subsequently been fires, Coppermine's vegetation has suffered little. The Maoris had small gardens there and left rock walls and field boundaries. There are today heavy forests of mature mahoe and puriri and tall stands of kanuka more varied in composition than any in the Hen and Chicken islands. The flora includes five species which are amongst the rarest in New Zealand.

Biologically more significant, however, is Coppermine's wildlife. Although the world's oldest living animal (the *tuatara*), the only surviving member of the dinosaurs, unchanged for more than 200 million years, occurs on eighteen small offshore islands in New Zealand, it is, except only on Coppermine and Stephen islands, barely surviving in the presence of rats and is an almost exclusively adult population of over fifty years of age. On Coppermine Island the *tuatara* (*Sphenodon punctatus*) thrives free from disturbance by the European rat, cats or fire.

On Coppermine Island there are also a number of species of rare indigenous birds. It is the most important breeding ground of the flesh-footed shearwater which, unlike the mutton-bird, is absolutely protected. It is a burrowing seabird which excavates tunnels and holes in well drained, light greywacke soils at the top of rock cliffs and shares its habitations with the *tuatara*. Also of ornithological importance is Pycroft's petrel, one of the rarest of sea birds. The North Island saddleback was recently transferred from Hen Island and established in the bush on Whatupuke Island which is now one of the four small islands where this species survives. The only other members of the ancient group of birds to which the endemic saddlebacks belong are the extinct *huia* and the rare *kakaho*.

The conservationists naturally objected to the proposed prospecting of the two Chicken islands and fought to persuade the government to deny a private mining concern the right to disrupt this unique and hitherto little disturbed fauna and flora. Mining, certainly, and prospecting, almost inevitably, would, they thought, lead to the introduction of rats quite apart from the disruption that must follow the cutting of access and the comings and goings of men, machines and equipment. To date both Coppermine and Whatupuke are free from rats, cats, goats, pigs, deer, opossums and other exotic pests found on the mainland and in some combination on all but very few offshore islands.

And so it is with other treasures which the wild landscape of a diminishing number of New Zealand offshore islands offers. Should Coppermine and Whatupuke be rigorously protected, or should they be sacrificed for a possible 150,000 tons of copper to be developed by capital domiciled outside New Zealand? This question was settled in 1969 when, after much delay, prospecting was allowed subject to safeguards. The prospectors found little of economic significance, and withdrew having done little damage.

The larger tracts of mainland wild landscape do not face the same immediate danger or similar risk of rapid transformation. But in the long run, if tourism is to become one of New Zealand's major earners of overseas currency, the very attractions which they have, may well be lost in their 'development'. New Zealand's problem appears to be not to decide whether 'progress' is to be allowed but whether the taming of the wild landscapes of the backblocks will be planned and organized so as to ensure that the manmade additions and modifications can be made to harmonize and to produce an amalgam that is aesthetically as appealing and satisfying as the original. After all, in a century and a quarter of European invasion, New Zealand has experienced such situations before and has emerged from the dilemma in the absence of conscious 'planning' not without success, as later chapters of this book will show.

Chapter 6
High country landscapes

'High country' is a term used in the South Island of New Zealand to refer to the land beyond the sharply delimited eastern front of the mountains which hems in and abruptly terminates the inland extent of the plains and downlands. In particular it has come to designate the jumble of dry tussock, bare grey rock, steep ranges, fault-edged structural plains and the flats of U-shaped valleys which have been occupied and whose 'natural' grazing land has been utilized for almost as long as the coastal plains themselves. But while the plains and downland of Marlborough, Canterbury and Otago have seen their farm landscape transformed at different times in response to changing prices, farm technology, transport and communications, the economy, the extensive grazing practices and the general appearance of the vast and towering landscape of the high country has changed little in twelve decades of European occupance.

Geomorphologically 'high country' embraces also the unoccupied alpine peaks and summits of permanent ice and snow above and beyond the grazing land; but in common usage – as here – the term is applied specifically to the grey-brown, föhn swept, sparsely occupied, inland domain of the runholders and their flocks.

This mountain vastness of tussock, occasional beech forest and elevated shrubland was 'spotted' and 'grid-ironed' and 'had the eyes taken out of it' in the 1850s. Within the confines of the land granted to the original settlement associations in Otago and Canterbury, land sales proceeded steadily under the Wakefield scheme at a 'uniform and sufficient' price. Outside these confines, however, land was first taken up in huge blocks of thousands of acres under leasehold pastoral licences. When the policy of free selection and purchase of land outside the settlements at low prices (five shillings an acre) came into operation after 1852, the leaseholding pastoralists used ingenious devices, together with the pre-emptive rights in their leases, to secure possession of the desirable areas controlling the economic operation of their runs. The runholders 'grid-ironed' key sections of their leaseholds, giving them private ownership of land without which the remainder of the runs was useless; or they 'spotted' all the desirable areas on their 10,000 to 50,000 acre leaseholds with freehold purchases. They were able to renew their leases without competition and thus virtually secured in perpetuity great landholdings on the easiest of terms.

8. *Upper Rangitata valley: Canterbury high country*
The extent and sweep of the glaciated pastoral high country landscape dwarfs the signs
of human occupance. On the dissected gravel fans in the foreground is the Mesopotamia
Homestead, and across the river on the projecting spur of the ranges at the river con-
fluence are the headquarters of the Erewhon station.

But before they occupied them, they had already usually burned their runs
charcoal black. This they did for two reasons: to rid the pastureland of spiny
shrubs and plants like 'wild irishman' (matagouri) which grew in dark thickets,
and speargrass, the sharp thick leaves of which pierced the legs and feet of
horses and runholders alike; and to promote fresh green palatable growth of the
otherwise brown, bunched tussock grasses. The Australian Merinos which the
pioneer squatters imported (overland at first from Nelson and Marlborough)
and which they depastured on the runs found the indigenous tussock species
of *Poa*, *Festuca* and *Chionochla* (the giant subalpine snowtussock) otherwise
unpalatable; but the fresh green shoots that followed a burn were both palatable
and nutritious. As a result regular, sometimes annual, burning of the runs became an established practice. Subsequently, now a century ago, rabbits were

established in New Zealand. They found the dry, sparsely occupied and frequently fired high country an ideal habitat. They came to occupy it in their millions. They were particularly numerous in the semi-arid tussock basins of Central Otago. With the repeated burning the hordes of rabbits helped reduce the extent, vigour and density of the tussock vegetation exposing more and more of the thin mountain soils. Without increase in the numbers of Merino sheep the runs became overstocked and overgrazed and, despite a noticeable fall in the number of livestock after 1875, the surface was increasingly exposed to erosion not only by periodic rainstorms of high intensity and short duration but by parched and persistent föhn winds and by frequent alternation of freeze and thaw. Sheltered interior valleys and basins of the high country have New Zealand's closest approach to a continental climate, have the greatest mean annual and daily range of temperature and experience ground frosts every month and as many as 200–250 a year. After the Merino and rabbit came deer, chamois and thar, carrying destruction and modification of the vegetation beyond where even hardy Merino wethers could go, thinning the beech forest understorey and browsing the subalpine scrub and herbfield associations.

The runholders' fires also destroyed some remnants of the beech forest which, before the occurrence of the fires that the moahunters had set a thousand years earlier, once occupied much more extensive areas on intermediate slopes. Here rainfall and soil moisture were greater and a close dark green mantle of mountain beech and even of podocarp forest had once hidden the stabilized greywacke scree and, from the time of the postglacial climatic optimum, had smoothed the contour of most rocky high country valleys and ranges. Throughout the high country, on valley walls, in shady gullies, on river flats and on terraced basin floors, the net and cumulative effects of Polynesian and European presence has been to bare thin and gravelly soils, to induce erosion, and to expose shingle and rock scree to gravitational creep. On the terrace flats of the schist grabens in Central Otago and the Mackenzie country, wind has stripped off much of the soil leaving behind an expanse of stones and little vegetation. The greywacke rock skeleton of the mountains of Canterbury and Marlborough is today more widely revealed and the landscape rawer, rougher and rockier than it was.

The lofty peaks and ridges, the U-shaped valleys, the naked exposure of the jointed greywacke sandstones, flagstone and argillite, the expanse of loose midslope scree, the gutted slides of angular shingle, the rock debris of alluvial fans and the expanses of bleached-white rounded riverbed boulders are pervading elements in the high country landscape. Others are the remaining indigenous and sparser introduced vegetation and the visible evidence of what, for New Zealand, is an unusual and locally sharply varying climate. The expanse of tussock dominated grassland – tawny under infrequent cloud and rain, russet in the sparkling frosty morning air and bright sunshine – dominates the valley floors and lower slopes and occupies the less severely eroded and broader stretches of river terraces in Central Otago and the Mackenzie country. On the deeper and more mature yellow-brown tussock soils of the valleys – especially in recent years with some use of artificial fertilizers and with oversowing of seed – European grasses and clovers as well as weeds like catsear have crept into the grassland and their seeds are sometimes carried by stock to considerable elevation.

In Central Otago, with irrigation, and elsewhere, with the cultivation and top-dressing of smaller paddocks close to homesteads and sheepyards, crops of turnips and rape are grown and stands of lucerne, or hay paddocks of ryegrass, cocksfoot and clover are established; and they form bright rectangles of changing shades of green in an expansive mountain-dominated landscape of stable and persistent hues of steel grey and straw brown. Where irrigation water is available, as in parts of the broader section of the high country in Central Otago, with its inland basins and fault bounded ranges of schist, where miners fossicked for gold in the 1860s and dug the hillside channels to bring sluice water to their alluvial diggings, the patches of green pasture are more extensive, more finely subdivided and more heavily stocked. Such is the case in the vicinity of Cromwell, in the Manuherikia valley between the Dunstan mountains and the Raggedy range, and in the crescent of artificially watered land at the foot of the Old Man range near Earnscleugh.

In the narrow section of the Clutha valley between Millers Flat and Roxburgh, where cold air drainage is more effective than on the flats of the terraced basins, and where frosts are thus confined to shallow layers close to the ground, the variety of alien and unusual colours in the high country scene is greater. Here irrigated orchards occur, stone fruit ripening to perfection. The seasonal rhythm of colour changes from bare blocks of black and leafless trees in winter, through the short season of profuse pink and white blossoming of apricots, cherries and apples, to the late summer greens and autumn tints of yellow-browns. This splash of changing colour occurs in a narrow strip bordering the river and is confined abruptly by the bare slopes of the dull brown and purple schists of the valley sides and their sparse and lighter coloured spatter of depleted tussocks.

The high country is however the vast and far-reaching domain of the 'squattocracy' of runholders. They still lease the majority of their individual properties from the Crown. But today the terms of their leases are more generous, of longer term, and more enlightened than they were a century ago. In the 1850s and 1860s an earlier generation of graziers, often forebears of the present holders, established a regime of depasturing sheep on the unfenced mountain range and a system of extensive grazing which, with the laxly supervised pattern of leasehold tenure, was largely responsible for an early deterioration of the native pastures and the induced erosion of the high country's thin and stony soils.

Throughout the mountain terrain, extending four hundred miles from the Wairau and Awatere valleys in Marlborough to the eastern shores of Lake Te Anau and Manapouri, the land is still held and operated in large holdings – typically of 10,000 to 50,000 acres with occasional much larger runs. Here are most of the 13 million acres in New Zealand which are officially classed as tussock grassland. More than 10 million acres of high country carry about 2·5 million sheep plus other stock. Half the sheep are Merinos: the rest Halfbreds and Corriedales. The high country tussock lands are farmed by only 300 or 400 graziers: they constitute less than 1 per cent of New Zealand farmers but occupy not less than 25 per cent of the occupied land in farms. And here are depastured possibly only 3 per cent of the country's livestock – at the average rate of one 'ewe equivalent' to 3 or 4 acres, or one-tenth only of the average carrying capacity of all the dominion's farms.

The high country runholder is thus lord of an extensive estate reaching over lofty ridges much further than his eye can see. The centre of his property is isolated even from that of his closest neighbour which lies typically on the other side of the 7,000 foot snow-ridged divide deep in the next valley and thirty or forty miles away by road. In earlier decades the homestead and its adjacent and associated residential buildings, housing manager, shepherds, general hands, musterers, cowman, gardener, rouseabout and itinerant gangs of shearers and other seasonal workers, constituted a self-contained world of its own – a world in which the occupier was king. Only rarely today are treacherous shingle rivers to be forded. Most stations are accessible by motor vehicle. Operations are mechanized, the labour force reduced and the permanent station population has declined from upwards of thirty to fewer than ten. The runholder is thus able to make frequent trips by car to Blenheim, Christchurch, Timaru or Dunedin to do his business and can attend race meetings, agricultural shows, farm auctions, stud sales, etc. much more frequently than in times which were economically more austere. His children still go to private boarding schools, however, and his wife may be absent at times to make her rounds of the fashionable social circles in town.

The high country runholders form one of the few clearcut and distinctive social groups in New Zealand and the run itself, one of the few places where society is clearly stratified. The high country runholders vie with the big sheep-farmers of the North Island East Coast and with the medical profession in the larger urban centres (themselves now rapidly acquiring their outer suburban green acres) as the most sharply differentiated social groups in the country – horsey, affluent and envied. But the runholder 'squattocracy's' prestige and political influence is not what it was when they dominated the economy and the government of the infant colony and its provinces a century ago. They may still exercise disproportionate power in agricultural circles, however, through their prominence on some of the country's more important agencies of economic power – on the New Zealand Wool Board and New Zealand Meat Producers' Board, for example.

How does the high country run function and what does it contribute to the life and landscape of its setting in a spacious mountain terrain? Its economy and system of management depend in part on its location and in part on the attitude – and age – of its holder. The more isolated runs, their unfenced grazing blocks running back to the ice and snow of the main divide, with a high proportion of winter country with southerly aspect and exposure, carry fewer sheep. They are still exclusively Merinos and the flock is made up very largely of wethers rather than breeding ewes. Supplementary feed or cultivated paddocks of pasture may be absent and the stock dependent entirely on indigenous grasses and such alien species as have accidentally been dispersed amongst the tussocks. Here the breeding of replacements may be difficult; wethers are usually bought-in, and in large numbers, especially after a bad season and heavy winter snow losses. Income is derived almost entirely from wool – fine Merino wools with a count greater than 60/64s and of high value per pound.

In the broader valleys nearer the front country and foothills where the mountain rivers debouch through rock gorges on to (or literally into) the gravel plains and terraced basins, the proportion of 'winter country' (low, sheltered and with warm and sunny northerly aspect) is greater. The river flats are wider, the shingle fans have gentle slopes. Their yellow-brown tussock soils are deeper and sometimes ploughable. Here close to the homestead are not only holding paddocks but also other relatively small, fenced enclosures where crops, lucerne hay and improved pastures of exotic grasses are grown. The hoggets and in-lamb ewes can be more generously fed and treated through the winter, lambing percentages are higher, the flock can be replaced, and surplus young stock produced for sale. Halfbred sheep or the inbred halfbred Corriedale breed, rather than the pure Merino, are run. The Halfbred is the product of running Lincoln, Leicester or Romney long woolled rams with Merino ewes to produce a longer, heavier, but somewhat coarser fleece, a wether that will fatten more readily and ewes suitable for crossing with the Southdown ram on lowland farms to produce export lamb. Here, too, cattle play an increasingly important part in the livestock economy. Whilst in the remote backcountry the native grazings support one dry sheep on from 5 to 10 acres, here on the better and often smaller runs the carrying capacity of the tussock blocks and improved paddocks may extend to one 'ewe equivalent' (allowing proportionately for cattle and young stock) to 2 or 3 acres.

The term 'run' ('sheeprun') is usually applied to a legally designated extent of private and leasehold land. The term 'station' ('sheep station') is applied to the economic enterprise carried out on the holding and sometimes to the heart of the operation centred on a diverse but nucleated cluster of buildings. The homestead, however, is the residence of the owner; or, in the case of absentee owners (rarer in these days of easy travel to town), the homestead is usually occupied by the manager and his family. Thus the word 'station' is used in naming the grazing enterprise and the location of its operational headquarters. Most of these names are those originally bestowed on the properties. Many are of Scottish origin, as were the early flock owners and their shepherds though they often came to New Zealand via Australia. Others commemorate local landmarks and landscape features. Such are Grampians, Glenmore, Braemar and Glentanner, Birch Hill and Whalesback stations. Better known outside New Zealand may be the upper Rangitata runs now named Erewhon station after Samuel Butler's literary work, although this property's original name Stronechrubie ('crooked spur') seems more appropriate. Butler named his own consolidated runs in the Rangitata valley Mesopotamia station.

The station homestead and its attendant buildings nestle squat and cosily in the valleys on gravel terraces or gentle alluvial fans close to the foot of mountain slopes, diminutive and inconspicuous against the massive backdrop of closer

9. *Glentanner station: Mackenzie country*
The massive woolshed, the homestead by the plantation of larch and pines, the sheep yards and holding paddocks, a small part of the Merino flock, and the tussock slopes beyond rising to a height of 8,000 feet in the Ben Ohau Range.

ranges and distant ice-capped peaks. They are most readily picked out by the dark cluster of exotic trees planted with care and grown with patience to provide shelter and to appease a nostalgia by providing a sign of home in the vastness of this strange, unoccupied and alien landscape. Many of the homesteads were built a century ago to replace temporary hutments erected hastily to provide evidence of occupance of the initial leasehold grants. They are snug, squat, timbered structures with overhanging eaves and wide verandahs 'and ample enough for a large family and the domestic servants as once befit the needs of the 'squattocracy'. Today the garden is choked with a variety of trees and shrubs from all corners of the earth amassed over the leisurely decades of loneliness, isolation and time on hand.

Close by, but at a sufficient distance, are the other buildings: the family home of the manager or overseer; accommodation for shepherds; the gardener's and rouseabout's cottage; and the shearers' quarters sufficient to shelter, feed and bunk a gang of ten or a dozen including blade shearers, fleecoes, wool classers, cooks, etc. The most important building is the woolshed, with its stands for up to eight shearers, and its adjacent counting-out yards. Alongside it are holding pens, drafting yards, sheep dip and overnight paddocks. Today there are other buildings and sheds to house tractors, landrovers, fertilizer, stores and bales of hay. Yet all this – a remote village to itself – may well be lost and difficult to see from an adjacent peak or ridge, so massive and majestic is its physical setting. So it is, too, with the gravel roads and station tracks and even with the railway line threading its way through the upper Waimakariri valley to Arthur's Pass. They are like spider-web-thin threads against the background when viewed as though on an oblique aerial photograph from lofty ridges on one of the station's outer tussock blocks.

On the more distant tussock grazing blocks, each of which may well be several thousand acres in extent and delimited with wire fences only where the absence of grazing, riverbeds, or rock gullies make fences necessary, there may be musterers' huts. These are used usually twice in the year when the flock is brought in for shearing or the autumn drafting at which time stock is judiciously switched according to its class and needs from summer to winter country. The musterers and shepherds spend the night in the huts and so get an early start at mustering difficult faces in order to have the sheep in the smaller homestead enclosures before dark. Such huts are also used by professional deer cullers and by mountain climbers.

The most valuable animals on the sheep stations are not the stud rams or prize bulls, the shepherds' sturdy hacks or even the runholder's favourite jumper or polo pony, but the sheep dogs. Without these alert, tough, hard-working animals – of all shapes, colours and sizes, but bred for their 'eye', bark, intelligence and obedience – the utilization of the high country runs for sheep or cattle grazing would be impossible. Every shepherd has a 'team' of dogs – 'eye' dogs, 'heading' dogs, 'huntaways' and general purpose dogs. And near the shepherds' quarters is a line of kennels. It is necessary to slaughter an old sheep every day or so to feed the dogs, and 'killers' are kept handy for 'dog tucker'.

Fundamentally the present grazing system is little different from what it was. In the last twenty years, however, there has been a change in attitude; and some significant details of management and practice have been modified so that a conservational economy is tending to replace a basically destructive one.

A representative high country sheep station with a reasonable proportion of winter country and several hundred acres of improved flats would in the later 1960s consist of approximately 30,000 acres, at least three-quarters of this being land held on leasehold tenure comprising several runs with different lease renewal dates. The tussock range – all of it leasehold – may well be subdivided with a minimum of six wire fences into six or seven 'blocks' ranging in size from 800 to 5,300 acres. The larger and more distant summer blocks are elevated and broken by extensive sheets of moving rock scree, deep gullies enclosing remnant patches of beech forest and rising beyond ridges of snow tussock to alpine herbfield vegetation and the snowline. Here winter grazing of all but the hardiest wethers would be fraught with risk of severe losses. The 600 acres of ploughable land, mainly on river terrace and soil-covered shingle cones or beside moraine-dammed mountain lakes, within a mile of the homestead and sheepyards, is nearly all freehold. Of its eight paddocks, all but one or two are improved. There are something in the order of 120 acres of animal fodder crops, mainly turnips, 80 acres of lucerne and the rest in European grasses grazed at lambing by the ewes and during autumn and winter by the ewe hoggets after the hay has been baled and shedded.

Sheep shorn total almost 10,000, nearly 30 per cent up on the number carried a generation ago. This is the result of the better care and feeding of both ewes and hoggets made possible by the vanquishing of the rabbit hordes and their grazing competition, and by the postwar (and especially post-1951 wool price boom) improvements. These may well include cultivation for supplementary winter feed, closer subdivision of paddocks, topdressing and surface-sowing of part of the closer blocks and their cutting in half by fences. Almost 200 Hereford cattle are likely to be wintered today where none was grazed before 1955.

Breeding ewes form 65 per cent of the Halfbred flock. A modest but rising lambing percentage of 82 produces well over 5,000 lambs of which almost half are held on as hoggets and as flock replacements. The wether lambs are disposed of as stores. Most are regularly purchased by the operator of a dry-sheep run as replacements for his wether flock. Only occasionally are wethers retained and later sold as two-tooths. Annual stock losses amount to 5 per cent; in years bad for snow this figure may be trebled. There are thus between 1,200 and 1,500 five-year-old cull ewes to dispose of each year. These, too, are largely sold privately in small lots to farmers on the plain who, using a Down ram, may raise from them in each of two seasons 100 per cent of 'Canterbury lamb'.

The ewes produce bare fleeces averaging almost 7 pounds in weight: two-tooth wethers may yield fleeces in excess of 10 pounds. With bellies, skirtings and oddments this relatively fine wool (60/64s), more than 80,000 pounds or 230 bales of it, accounts on average for just over 50 per cent of the station's gross income although this varies erratically as does the auction price of wool. Sales of lambs, hoggets and cast-for-age ewes together provide one-third of the gross income: store cattle account for the rest – a steeply rising proportion.

The progress made with the rehabilitation of the high country montane tussock grassland since the depredations of eighty years of occupance became clearly established and widely recognized, is no better illustrated than by Molesworth. In 1938 the Molesworth station comprised three large runs (Molesworth, 127,600 acres; Tarndale, 112,000 acres; and Rainbow, 76,000 acres) which had been operated as one unit for fifty-five years. At that date the runs were handed back to the Crown, their owner unable to continue to graze them profitably in view of the deterioration of the vegetative cover, the falling carrying capacity, the recurrent disastrous snow losses, the devastation of rabbits and the low prices during the 1930s for fine wools. The property is supposed to have carried 70,000 sheep in the 1880s and 1890s. In the first decade of this century sheep shorn fluctuated about 45,000. When the lease was surrendered only 23,000 sheep were sold off. In 1949 the neighbouring station, St Helens (comprising two runs – St Helens, 134, 800 acres and Dillon, 77,300 acres) reverted to the Crown. Although the sheep population had been as high as 47,000 in 1932–33, only 13,250 sheep were sold on the station's abandonment.

Rainbow was re-leased in 1939. Since 1940, when the Department of Lands and Survey took over responsibility for grazing and rehabilitating the country, after two years of rabbit destruction by the Department of Agriculture, the policy pursued has been essentially one of restoration under light grazing. At first Molesworth and Tarndale were farmed as a unit. Later St Helens and Dillon were added. The operational unit called Molesworth station now comprises 458,000 acres of high country. It lies in the headwaters and upper catchments of the Clarence, Awatere and Wairau valleys and astride the boundaries of the Marlborough, Nelson and Canterbury Land Districts. The homestead on the upper Awatere is eighty miles from Blenheim. It is in fact only twenty miles from Kaikoura but between it and the sea to the southeast are the Inland and Seaward Kaikoura ranges, 7,000 and 8,000 feet above sea level. Lying well to the east of the broad belt of mountains, and deeply sheltered from the west, southwest and southeast, the Molesworth country is drier than much of the high country and more continental, rainfall falling to 25–27 inches on the valley flats and frosts reaching an average of 230 a year at the homestead. Erratic heavy falls of snow, from southeasterly winds are, however, rather frequent. Management is not easy. Availability of winter feed sets limits to productivity.

At first the grazing policy substituted on Molesworth for the traditional use and practice in the high country was revolutionary and experimental. The first objective was to exterminate rabbits and deer. This has been virtually accomplished by poisoning and shooting. Burning has been rigidly controlled. The most important innovation, however, was the substitution of beef cattle for sheep.

In the new ecological conditions the vegetation has changed spectacularly. The recovery of tussock grasses and of intertussock species – often palatable indigenous grasses like the blue wheat grass (*Agropyron scrabrum*) – has been remarkable. But as in other parts of the highland where rabbits have been severely reduced in number there has been a striking spread of sweet brier, formerly nibbled by rabbits and now untouched by cattle. Sheep once kept broom in check. Now it constitutes a problem; and ragwort, a weed of much laxly grazed dairy land, especially in damper environments, is spreading along roads and tracks.

More recently vegetational change has been hastened by the aerial oversowing of cocksfoot and clovers on 50,000 acres of the easier slopes. The runs taken over in 1940 were initially stocked with 723 head of mixed Aberdeen Angus and Hereford cattle. The herd slowly built up to 2,500 by natural increase and purchase. With the incorporation of St Helens, the size of the herd climbed to 4,800. In 1967 it totalled 9,000 head, including 2,643 breeding cows. The annual sale of two- and three-year-old steers ranges up to a thousand head. In addition cull cows and surplus heifers are annually sold. All cattle are driven seventy-five miles to the railhead at Culverden and railed to Addington saleyards in Christchurch. The store cattle command favourable prices and are eagerly sought as they handle and fatten well down-country.

Despite the deliberate pursuit of an expensive and experimental conservation programme, and after meeting the costs of weed and rabbit control and paying interest charges, the Molesworth cattle grazing operation has been both an economic and ecological success. Now that capital expenditure on development and rehabilitation have largely been met, Molesworth is indeed highly profitable. It has not solved the high country's problems, but it has pointed a way to their solution. Molesworth will soon carry 10,000 head of cattle, well in excess in ewe equivalents of the sheep carried on the same property at the surrender of the various leases. It has a denser and more vigorous vegetation cover and the extent and activity of soil erosion have been diminished. The cover is not always an ideal or desirable one. The new weed problem is increasingly obvious and a return to sheep grazing would not solve it. Yet by grazing 90,000 sheep, which the property could now well support without threat to the tussocks or reacceleration of soil erosion processes, ragwort and broom could well be reduced and sweet brier's spread slowed down: but this would require different patterns of fencing, new capital investment in buildings, and a redesign of grazing policies and seasonal operations. Labour requirement would also be much heavier and more costly. Restocking would be expensive and require five years or more. New fencing would cost more than $500,000 and take ten years to build. But with the fall in returns from wool after 1965 and the increasing profitability of beef cattle, the established pattern of the Molesworth revolution appears to become sufficiently profitable for the weed problem to be attacked economically, not by changing the kind and ratios of livestock, but by new chemicals sprayed from the air.

Apart from its natural grazing and the minute island of improved pasture, fruit orchards and irrigated hay and crop land (in Central Otago), the high country has few other resources. Briefly, in the 1860s alluvial gold proved a bonanza in the parched and frosty basins of Central Otago and the narrow terraced valley heads beyond. But, apart from timber-constructed, and later steel-built, electrically operated bucket dredges which here and there continued to excavate the terrace gravels until the 1950s to leave behind a desert of boulders, and to win in the process a diminishing harvest of the precious metal, the known metallic mineral resources of this vast inland domain were exhausted very early after being picked over by immigrant Chinese diggers in the 1870s.

Although a menace, rabbits were turned to profit; of the annual shipment of rabbit skins which in 1894 reached almost 18 million, 80 per cent were exported through Dunedin and many of them came from rabbit 'farming' in the high country. Even as late as the 1930s and 1940s, and despite the largely ineffective introduction of myxomatosis, the country was exporting more than 10 million skins and 2 million carcasses a year. A cautious estimate made in 1950 suggested that more than 20 million rabbits were killed; that they ate as much as 2 million sheep, and caused a net loss of pastoral production worth more than $4 million.

In 1947 the policy of destroying rather than 'farming' rabbits had won the day. The Rabbit Destruction Council was established and devalued rabbit skins and carcasses by preventing their sale and export. Working through rabbit boards (which by the 1960s covered the whole country), it adopted an all-year-round 'killer policy' in an attempt to eradicate the pest. It was largely successful. The boards employed traditional methods – guns, traps, cyanide fumigation, and the spreading of phosphorized pollard and arsenic carrot baits – and also used aerial methods of distributing annually thousands of tons of poison baits. There was an impressive diminution in the numbers of the pest, but no extermination. It is safe to say that the carrying capacity of New Zealand pastures has been increased as a result by the equivalent of 2 million sheep. Much of this is to be attributed to the drier tussock grazing lands. This is the single most important 'improvement' that has occurred in the high country in the postwar period of renewal and conservation.

Water and scenery (including sports facilities) are the high country's only other resources in the light of contemporary technology, demands and appraisals. The scenery and the opportunities for recreation and sport within the high country cannot be divorced from those of the alpine wilderness beyond, which have been discussed in the previous chapter. Water, however, is derived mainly from air masses from the Tasman Sea and from west of the divide and more immediately from the summer and autumn melt of ice and snow in the alpine ranges. It passes through the high country, flowing in braided channels over the wide shingle beds of snowfed rivers – Clutha, Waitaki, Rangitata, Rakaia, Waimakariri, Waiau, Awatere and Wairau – on its way to the sea. It is in the high country that it is harnessed for power or channelled to irrigate Otago terraces and Canterbury plains.

Most spectacular are the chain of hydroelectric power stations on the Clutha river and the network of lakes, dams and power stations in the Mackenzie country and on the Waitaki. Until recently the expanding and largely North Island-based New Zealand economy has relied very largely for its inanimate energy on the water power resources of the Waikato river, Lake Taupo and the Volcanic Plateau. But with the increased costliness of harnessing the remaining potential hydro-power in the North Island, and with the laying on the ocean floor of the Cook Strait cable, attention has been diverted to the South Island's much more extensive and economically cheaper sources of water power. Since 1956 three South Island stations (on the Waitaki and Clutha rivers) have come into operation and have a capacity twice that of the six smaller stations constructed in the North Island in the same time. Moreover, the Manapouri project and the planned development of the water power of the upper Waitaki will double the South Island's generating capacity within a decade.

On the lower Waitaki, and within the high country, there are dams already, and manmade lakes behind them, at Waitaki (105 MW), Benmore (540 MW) and Aviemore (220 MW). The future will see a planned and integrated extension of the storage capacity of Lakes Ohau, Pukaki and Tekapo in the Mackenzie Basin and the erection of a chain of stations with an ultimate additional capacity of between 700 and 1000 MW.

These natural glacial lakes receive their waters largely from the summer melt of ice and snow. Their outflow to the Waitaki headwaters has a pronounced seasonal rhythm being lowest in winter when power demands are high. A small power station already exists at the outlet of Lake Tekapo. The proposal is to divert its tailrace flow from the present riverbed in a canal via Maryburn and through a tunnel to a point 400 feet above the present level of Lake Pukaki. Its fall over the edge of a 190 foot terrace at Maryburn and its downward plunge in penstocks to Lake Pukaki would supply two powerhouse sites. It is proposed to replace the present control dam at Lake Pukaki and raise the lake level 100 feet thus flooding 13,000 acres of the better tussock land on twelve sheep runs. From Pukaki the combined flow of the Tekapo canal and of the Pukaki river below the lake's present outflow would be carried by canal towards Lake Ohau where, in combination with the diverted flow of the Ohau river, it would generate 250 MW of power at Ostler before discharge into the Ohau river. Lower down the Ohau riverbed the plan envisages a concrete dam to divert the now combined flow from the three regulated lakes into a 200 foot-wide canal along the gravel terraces at the foot of the eastern slopes of the Benmore range. On its way to the artificial Benmore Lake (which now extends back almost fifteen miles above the Benmore dam) the regulated massive volume of water would pass through two more power stations generating 420 MW.

There is naturally concern among runholders – and in urban conservation circles – at this proposed development of high country water resources, especially since much of the construction work and disturbance of the landscape must take place at the very approach and portal to the Hermitage and Mount Cook National Park. The final answer will no doubt lie in dollars and cents. At present retail prices the potential supply of electricity from the Mackenzie Basin would be worth $40 million a year. Although it could be much increased, the present gross returns from all the grazing properties in the Mackenzie country tussock lands affected by the proposals is not more than $1 million a year – even less with the fall since 1967 in wool prices.

Scenically, there are two valid objections to the proposals. They will leave the present wide, white shingle beds of the Pukaki and Tekapo rivers and a few miles of the Ohau riverbed devoid of water when it is obliged to course through concrete lined canals. Secondly, the stark and beautiful glacial Lakes Tekapo, Pukaki and Ohau will become extensive man-controlled storage reservoirs. They will be filled to capacity by later summer meltwaters, but thereafter their levels will be lower as the stored water is drained off in response to distant cities' fluctuating demands for light and power, especially during the following winter in order to maintain or increase the flow of water throughout the chain of nine powerhouses down to the Waitaki station at Kurow. The lake levels will vary through a range of upwards of fifty feet, leaving at low water a wide and unsightly 'beach'. Although the manmade lakes will contribute to the quality and variety of the scene in the Ohau and Waitaki valleys, there will be detrimental interference with the natural, extensive sheets of sparkling blue waters of the Mackenzie lakes in which the reflected view of the snow-white peaks along the rampart of the Southern Alps is now a major attraction. Judicious planting of a variety of suitable trees will no doubt obviate the worst effects. But again one of the charms and peculiarities of the Mackenzie is its bare, hard and unbroken treeless vistas – despite the sixty-year-old urgent appeal of a prominent runholder to his compatriots (commemorated in a monument at the Burke's Pass entry to the high country) to 'plant trees for your life'.

Here and there the South Island high country landscape is being changed at the hands of man. These visually impressive – and economically significant – changes are, however, narrowly localized. In the vast scale of the tussock mountain country they are still puny even if they cost millions of dollars, take years to accomplish, and involve temporary beehives of human settlement and of mechanical activity. In overall appearance the broad expanse of mountainous terrain, interrupted and variegated by exposures of bedrock, loose grey angular rock rubble, sparse tussock, green paddocks, black hangers of beech trees, blue skeins of rivers, and diminutive state electricity plant maintenance 'villages', and clusters of sheep station buildings, has remained largely immutable.

Recent developments in land and station policy will reinforce this changelessness. With the establishment of catchment boards under the Soil Conservation and Rivers Control Act of 1941, and their subsequent belated discovery that their problems were rooted in the tussock catchments and that river stopbanks on the plains were merely palliatives; and with their firm control of the time and frequency of the grass and scrub fires the runholders were permitted to light; with enlightened administration by the Lands Department of the Crown leases and the encouragement of improvements and of raising carrying capacity on safe country; with the virtual conquest of the century-old rabbit pest and the reinvigoration of tussock growth, the widespread agencies of subtle change have been arrested. All these and other signs of acceptance of the conservation and national park movements should ensure a persistence of the high country's landscape and personality with little fear of marked or widespread deleterious change.

Chapter 7
Volcanic Plateau landscapes

In the North Island of New Zealand the narrow belt of axial ranges lies well to the east. Fault-bounded, their greywacke sandstones and argillites deeply dissected by running water and mass movement rather than by glacial abrasion, forested or scrub-covered to their summits, the ranges occupy in a successive suite a much smaller proportion of the total area than do the contrasting mountain terrains in the South Island. Such are the Rimutaka, Tararua, Ruahine, Kaimanawa, Kaweka, Huiarau and Raukumara ranges. Ignoring its peninsular projections, the North Island's shape and proportions are much more rectangular than the larger, bulkier, loftier, and more elongated outline of the South Island. While the mass of the South Island is built of broken and rocky mountains and its backbone and ribbed structure of bedrock are widely exposed, much of the North Island's interior has subdued plateau forms and its skeleton is deeply padded by younger and softer rocks. Even these are widely draped in a recently ejected cover of volcanic ash comprising a successive series of sheets of rhyolite pumice, much of it (Kaharoa) spread as recently as human times and most of it (Taupo) in any case not more than 2,000 years ago.

On three sides the Volcanic Plateau is shut in by more elevated country. From this point of view it is a basin rather than a plateau. It terminates eastwards in the blue and purply haze of the faulted front of the axial ranges. To the west it is shut off from the dissected hill country of Taranaki and inland Wanganui by the Rangitoto and Hauhungaroa ranges, a few hundred feet above the plateau's average elevation; to the southwest it is overlooked beyond Lake Taupo by the towering triplet volcanoes of the National Park. To the northwest, however, the eroded ignimbrite sheets of the Volcanic Plateau itself stand above the tributaries of the Waipa, Waikato and Waihou which tumble down through ash-coated hills to the lower downs and alluvial flats of the dairy lands; to the northeast the plateau overlooks the finely dissected narrow ridges and valleys which descend to the Bay of Plenty. For the most part the plateau has an elevation in excess of 1,200 feet. Its surface is faulted and fractured. Lake Taupo largely fills a faulted collapsed basin or graben, running northeast-southwest. Tabular surfaces lie at different elevations. The Rangitaiki valley is a shallow northeast-southwest extending terraced depression: west of it the Kaingaroa plateau formerly stood stark and open, its undisturbed sheets of ignimbrite heavily mantled in pumice and extending fifty miles without break of slope. The

Mamakus form a still largely forested upstanding plateau surface of ignimbrite. At Tarawera there are rough piles of recent volcanic debris, still rilled and gullied and not fully vegetated since their deposition less than a century ago, and huge rifts and gashes of explosive origin; elsewhere there are lake basins and depressions and, around every corner, over every hill, puffs of steam, boiling springs, mud pools, hot lakelets, and other signs of volcanism and structural instability.

Beneath the yellow, yellow-brown and chocolate sequences of layered ash and raw grey pumice, the solid rock is ignimbrite, rarely exposed except in the bed of major streams, or in vertical bluffs of fault faces, or in cliffed walls of stream-cut gorges, but responsible for the terraced and tabular appearance of otherwise near-flat plateau surfaces. Ignimbrite probably originated as an explosively erupted ash. Once fluffy and powdery, it now forms chemically uniform, hard, horizontal, acid layers of rock. Some 2,000 cubic miles of it remain, warped, fractured, regularly eroded, its columnar structure exposed only in the vertical cliffs and elsewhere smoothed and carpeted with brown layers of pumice ash.

The surface layers of rhyolitic ash are the product of very recent ejections, mainly from the vicinity of Lake Taupo, which probably occupies the surface of a collapsed section of the plateau. In 2,000 years much of the loose acid deposit of eruptive pumice showers has been carried off by the Waikato, Rangitaiki and other rivers and is now redeposited on river and coastal flats well beyond the plateau's rim. The blanket of ash gradually thins, from scores of feet near the Taupo source to a few inches. It can be traced, thin, tattered and threadbare, over the ranges and as far as the east coast. The light, porous, trace-element deficient soils derived from Taupo and Kaharoa ash have long delayed the plateau's economic development.

Elevated, bleak, exposed, infertile and often devoid of forest, and even of scrub where recent ash showers had interred an earlier vegetation, the interior plateau had little attraction a thousand years ago for the early Polynesian immigrant. He preferred the North Island's warm coasts and forested valleys, and found the plateau uninviting. Indeed its continued volcanic activity and, judging by the absence of gizzard stones and moa bones, its apparent lack of moas, made it a place to be avoided. It is tempting to speculate that the moa itself may have learned to avoid what subsequently the agriculturalist termed 'stock sick', cobalt-deficient soils of the plateau.

Later the Maori people, who competed and even fought for the North Island's more desirable habitats, and who had time to explore and utilize a wider basis of indigenous resources than their moahunter and largely South Island-based predecessors, found the North Island interior habitable. Indeed the Arawa people developed here one of Polynesia's more elaborate forms of artistic accomplishment. Maori settlement, however, was concentrated on lake shores (especially where nature provided hot water for cooking and other uses), along the banks of rivers, especially the Waikato, and on the rim of the ancient forest undisturbed by more recent eruptions particularly to windward, to the west, where the Hauhungaroa and Rangitoto ranges rose above the expansive plateau surfaces of scrub and tussock 'deserts'. It was the lakes, rivers, and forests that offered resources. Until the Maori acquired the European potato he was unable to practise agriculture in the frosty interior plateau climate and on light droughty pumice soils. It was probably only when the Irish potato reached the interior of the North Island – and replaced the kumara 'imported' as a luxury from the coastal territories and gardens of other tribes – that the Arawa and Tuwharetoa people cleared scrub, fern and forest with fire and, as a consequence, here and there checked nature's patient endeavours to clothe the pumice ash with forest. When Dieffenbach, Bidwill and Hochstetter first penetrated and reported on the plateau after 1839, they described extensive and recent damage by fires set by the Maori tribesmen.

In the first half century of European settlement, few immigrants made the difficult and roundabout journey to the plateau. It was remote, isolated, and difficult of access from all the coastal centres of early economic activity. Missionaries came first. From their earliest field of endeavour in the Bay of Islands they moved south, and by 1835 they had coastal stations as far south as Kawhia and Tauranga. They penetrated the interior from Tauranga without delay. Missions were established and staffed at Rotorua in 1835, and at Taupo in 1853. Both became the nuclei of the subsequent growth of European towns. Rotorua soon developed as the centre of European influence on the plateau. This it owed, not to the soils and agriculture of its vicinity, but to the spectacular volcanic and hydrothermal oddities and curiosities within the shallow caldera, occupied largely by Lake Rotorua, and of adjacent parts of the tableland. Rotorua was the point of departure by rutted and dusty pumice tracks for the sinter terraces at Rotomahana, and for the hot springs at Waiotapu and Wairakei. Before it acquired additional functions and services as a result of the human transformation of the plateau's resources and potentialities, it was for sixty years by far the best known and one of the very few settlements in New Zealand based on infant tourist and recreational industries. It was essentially a Victorian spa, attracting not only wealthy colonials to its thermal baths, but also curious visitors from other countries, drawn to Rotorua also by its boiling mudpools, steam vents, hot springs, spouting geysers, Maori maidens in flax skirts, and by the famous pink and white sinter terraces at Rotomahana, destroyed abruptly in 1886 by the Tarawera eruption.

The traffic remained small, however, because of the continued difficulty of access to the North Island interior. The railhead remained at the military post at Drury for some time, reached Mercer in 1875, Hamilton in 1879, and penetrated to Tirau and Putaruru on the northern fringe of the plateau in the year of the Tarawera eruption. It did not reach Rotorua until 1894. Meanwhile visitors to the thermal wonderland were dependent on steamer services from Auckland to Tauranga and, from there to Rotorua, on infrequent coaches with three horses in the lead and two on the pole. Goods were carried over pumice tracks by bullock wagon.

Although they contributed to the growth and to the specialized form and function of the infant Rotorua, tourists and those who took the baths there had little impact on the extensive landscapes of the Volcanic Plateau. Indeed they saw but a corner of it. Its real pioneers were a handful of pastoralists. After the Maori Wars and the Te Kooti disturbances their sparse flocks and herds shared the immense holdings with wild horses and cattle and wandering bands of Maoris – at Tihoi, north of Lake Taupo; at Lochinver, Taharua and Te Haroto, west of the Napier-Taupo road; at Rununga, east of it, and on the upper Rangitaiki river; at Galatea in the mid-Rangitaiki valley; and at Broadlands, Strathmore and Reporoa between Rotorua and Taupo. The earliest pastoralists were squatters without titles; others bought directly from the Maori and had irregular titles; some leased Maori land; few had legal road access to their 30,000 to 125,000 acre properties and could only get stock on to them by trespass over the land of other stations or over Maori territory.

They depastured sheep – mainly Merinos, sometimes Cheviots – on unfenced and unsubdivided land occupied variously, sparsely and often in stunted form by tussock on the exposed plateau surfaces, by manoao (*Dracophyllum*) in the wide low valleys, by manuka and kanuka, flax, raupo, rushes and niggerhead, fern and tutu (*Coriaria*). To the west on the hills, beside the Waikato in the valley, and on the Mamaku plateau, native bush had sometimes survived the fires that accompanied the fall-out of hot ash; and here and there a second growth of *Gaultheria*, *Coprosma*, *Pittosporum*, lancewood and five finger was invading the shrubland in a valiant attempt to clothe the infant pumice soil in forest.

The pioneer pastoralists burned large areas of scrub. In autumn the fern, manoao and manuka carried fire fiercely over the parched and open surface of pumice. But little seed was sown. The expanse of low vegetation, burnished and coppery against the purple background of distant ranges, was transformed into a drab ash wilderness of grey and black. Only slowly did it turn green with the June and July rains and the volunteer growth of sparse grasses. After the winter frosts juvenile scrub species and reduced tussocks alone survived. Stock did poorly. Losses of hoggets and young cattle were high and the natural increase in livestock numbers painfully slow. Pumice soils earned the reputation of being 'bush sick' and 'stock sick'. Markets were distant; the isolation 'truly terrible'. Properties frequently changed hands. Others were abandoned. Not until the land was ploughed and fertilizers expensively brought in by bullock wagon and drays did the plateau soils here and there show a glimmer of promise. It was after the century's turn that the growth of turnips and hay enabled small numbers of sheep to be wintered successfully. Only on soils derived from later ash deposits – the Rotomahana 'mud' for example – and from alluvium – at Ngongotaha and elsewhere beside Lake Rotorua and in the Reporoa valley – were small holdings permanently established and a few dairy cows kept. At the century's turn the rhyolitic pumice ash of the interior plateau still formed an extensive unoccupied 'desert' of scrub with the reputation of being unable to support 'a grasshopper to the acre'. The way was open for its planting in trees.

After the struggle with the Maori over land had ended in the confiscation of large areas, most of the North Island was ripe for settlement. With the stimulus provided by refrigerated shipping and the enthusiasm of landless South Islanders seeking to establish smallholdings in the north, the forest domain on the downland, dissected hill country and more accessible mountain slopes in the North Island, was ruthlessly and rapidly stripped of its natural cover. In the last thirty years of the century hundreds of thousands of acres of dense bush fell each year to the settler's axe, or was transformed into a ghostly wilderness of gaunt black stumps by autumn fires that blazed for days and smouldered for weeks. The clearance was pushed into vulnerable watersheds which, within a generation, ruined fortunes and stout hearts, and were abandoned. There was little or no concern either for future timber supplies or for watershed protection.

Only in 1921 was the State Forest Service, the predecessor of the present New Zealand Forest Service, created, its objectives to protect and manage the remaining indigenous forest and to establish exotic substitutes for the mammoth wealth of forest timbers wasted and destroyed.

Given the decision to plant, and to replace wasted indigenous timbers with exotics, little time was lost. Indeed afforestation was undertaken at too great a speed and with too little thought and planning. Practically all of it was concentrated on the Volcanic Plateau. Here pioneer pastoralists and earlier government experiments (as at Whakarewarewa in 1898) had shown that the pumice soils would grow better trees than livestock. Here were enormous areas of unoccupied land – often held by the Crown – near-flat or rolling, broken by few steep slopes, covered only by scrub and stunted vegetation, easily cleared by fire and its regrowth not vigorous enough to submerge seedling trees, unwanted for agriculture, expansive, open, available. In 1925 the government announced its intention of planting 300,000 acres. At the same time a large number of bond-selling, tree-planting companies sprouted and mushroomed, acquired cheap land and began planting. Planting reached a crescendo in the late 1920s. In a decade from 1926 to 1936, the basis was laid by prison labour and unemployed relief workers for a transformation first of the landscape and later of the economy of the Volcanic Plateau. In all, not far short of a million acres of conifers – principally *Pinus radiata* – have been planted in the pumice.

Large expanses of the dull grey-brown frosty wilderness of the Kaingaroa plateau have been converted into uninterrupted green-black stands of mature

10. *Volcanic Plateau, Kaingaroa*

Part of 'the world's largest man-made forest'. The planting of radiata pine over 30 years ago transformed the unused scrub and tussock landscape. The unplanted 'island' (right of centre) accommodates the special foresters' settlement of Kaingaroa. In the distance the volcanic cone of Ruapehu marks the southwestern limit of the plateau.

trees. Today, geometrically rectangular blocks of regimented battalions of conifers restrict the view but themselves stretch for scores of miles. Elsewhere smaller state plantations of Douglas fir and of Corsican and ponderosa pine spread over low hills; and the pale autumn ochre of larch and the odd clumps of shimmering golden poplar add variety to the tree-hemmed landscape. The private plantations – almost entirely of the fast-growing Californian radiata (or Monterey) pine – have been set out in smaller blocks and principally on the northwestern fringe of the plateau in more broken country where the Waikato and its tributaries have notched gorges and valleys in the ignimbrite. Here along the State Highway No. 1 between Tokoroa and Atiamuri, the forest plantings climb steep slopes of pumice breccias and poorly compacted ignimbrite, hang on bluffs of rhyolite flows, hem in the Waikato river and encircle manmade lakes created to supply hydroelectric power stations.

To reap the harvest of fast maturing softwood timber – and to do it before too much of the single age group pines become overmature and ravaged by insect and fungus pests – giant sawmills and integrated timber, pulp and paper mills have been erected either on the plateau or just beyond its margins – at Waipa (Rotorua), Whakatane, Kawerau and Kinleith. Where necessary, towns have been laid out – as at Kawerau, Murupara and Tokoroa – and they are among the most modern, most carefully planned and fastest growing in New Zealand. To facilitate the extraction and delivery of logs to the mills or to ports, and to speed the delivery of timber products to centres of consumption and export, new roads and railways have been constructed. The roads serve today not only the timber interests, but the farmers who have more recently come to the plateau, the booming hydroelectric construction camps and the more permanent powerhouse maintenance villages. They also provide much easier, more comfortable and greater variety of access for the swelling volume of tourists and holidaymakers which an affluent and motorized age brings to the lakes and thermal attractions, and to the winter sports grounds, or who seek solitude, recreation and adventure in the trout fishing and pig and deer hunting which the North Island interior offers in such profusion.

11. *Volcanic Plateau: land development and landscape transformation*
Crushing of light scrub with water-filled flanged rollers before burning, seeding and aerial topdressing.

But the fever of afforestation has still not taken more than a quarter of the plateau's extent. When the economic depression reduced planting to a crawl there were still hundreds of thousands of acres of land for use and development if the incentive could be provided and if appropriate techniques could be devised. In 1936 the cause of 'bush sickness' – a wasting disease of ruminant livestock – was tracked down and a remedy provided. The persistent failure of livestock to thrive on pastures based on soils derived from Taupo and Kaharoa rhyolitic ash proved to be due to a mineral trace-element deficiency, most readily remedied by applying cobalt in minute quantities to the topsoil. With the post-war development and subsequent refinement of methods of applying fertilizers from the air, a technology was at hand not only for spreading phosphates cheaply over extensive areas of variable terrain but for evenly applying the necessary trace elements at the same time.

Institutional innovations had also been made that opened up the possibility of land development as soon as the war was over. Back in 1929 legislation had enabled the state to undertake development of Crown land as distinct from merely providing access to it and disposing of unimproved sections. By 1931 the first 1,100 out of 8,000 acres of light pumice land on the Ngakuru block near Rotorua had been cleared and grassed. First the depression, and then the war, prevented expanded land development by the state; later, with the need to settle returned servicemen, the solution to the problem of 'bush sick' land, and clarification in 1941 of administrative procedures with the establishment within the Lands and Survey Department of the Land Settlement Board and the Land Development Branch, the scene was set for another major transformation of landscape on the Volcanic Plateau.

In Rotorua and Taupo counties alone 433,000 acres were set aside or acquired by the Crown for development. Subsequently the land available has been substantially extended by the Department of Maori Affairs which has instituted and pursued a similar policy of large-scale land development. It now utilizes the organization of the Land Development Branch in carrying out its programme of farm settlement of hitherto unused Maori land for the benefit of the Maori people.

By 1967, when the programme was slowed first by the slump in wool prices and subsequently by the reduction of the basic payout price for butterfat, 210,000 acres of land had been developed, subdivided, alienated and settled, adding 585 dairy farms and 262 sheep farms, a total of 847 units, or 75 per cent of all farm holdings in Taupo and Rotorua counties. At the same time the Land Development Branch had 250,000 acres of land on hand of which 171,000 acres were farmed by the state in the process of further development. The state has indeed in the postwar years been the largest farmer and holder of livestock in New Zealand. In 1967 it was running 280,000 breeding ewes, 255,000 lambs, hoggets and other dry sheep, 27,000 run cows and heifers, and nearly 60,000 dry

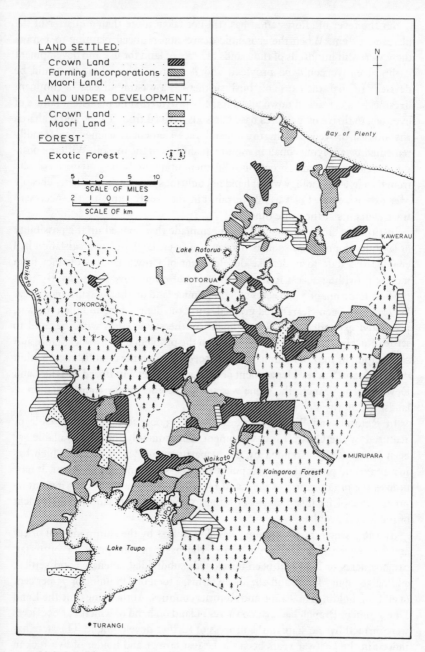

12. *Volcanic Plateau*

cattle on the Volcanic Plateau alone.* This is little less than a third of all the sheep, and is more than half of all the beef cattle, on the plateau.

The 'development' of land for farming in New Zealand has everywhere involved the supplanting of an indigenous vegetative cover of bush, swamp, scrub or tussock that had known no grazing pressure other than that of the moa, by an alien array of pasture grasses and clovers, or of arable crops. Only where the replacement has been complete has the development been wholly successful. At times native species have reasserted themselves so vigorously that the individual pioneer has been compelled to abandon the struggle to suppress them. The development for pastoral farming of huge tracts of tussock, scrub and fern on the Volcanic Plateau mainly in the last decade differs from the previous pattern of winning land for agriculture not in its objective, or indeed its methods, but in its planning, precision, large-scale organization and complete mechanization. It is accomplished in three stages: the initial (or grassing) stage; the stage of consolidation (or large-scale 'station' farming); and the stage of subdivision, disposal and individual settlement. At each stage of development the transformed and ephemeral character of the landscape has its distinctive features. All stages are to be seen at present on different parts of the plateau, the landscape of which is in the process of staged alteration. Dynamic change is much more in evidence here than in any other part of the country.

The first phase of development goes into operation after careful survey of the contour, soils and vegetation of the country to be broken in, after a 'scheme plan' has been made for its taming, and after funds have been budgeted for its subjugation by machines and livestock and its subsequent settlement. The budget of the Rotorua office of the Land Development Branch alone amounts to $5 million a year. A section of 3,000 acres may be tackled in the first year – one-quarter or one-fifth of the total area of a development block. Light scrub and fern are crushed by giant rollers dragged by caterpillar tractors. Heavy manuka and second growth, even scattered volunteer radiata pines, are torn out of the ground and flattened by a massive battleship chain on which are enormous three-quarter ton steel balls tugged from each end by heavy duty tractors. This crushing is done in winter or spring, depending on the weather, though the porous pumice soils allow heavy machinery to work at most times of the year. The following summer the torn and tattered vegetation is burned, after which super giant discs break the soil, cut up any roots and turn in the ash from the fires. The discs are followed by rollers. On easy slopes a selected grass-clover seed mixture is sown by machines. On low hill country and steep faces the mixture is aerially sown and the ground subsequently harrowed. Seeding is done after the hard frosts of the winter are over – a year after crushing. Rolling

* In New Zealand as a whole on 1 July, 1968 the Department of Lands had almost 600,000 acres in grass on which it ran 1,560,000 sheep and 220,000 run cattle. It produced 15 million lb of wool worth almost $3,650,000 even at the depressed prices obtaining at the time.

and early stocking of the first strike of grass are important for compaction and consolidation of the pumice soils. Indeed livestock in the correct numbers and of the appropriate type at different stages are the principal tools of trade of the land developer.

One of the first auxiliary tasks is to provide road access to the operation head-quarters, and to bulldoze tracks over the block. Before sowing, an airstrip must be prepared, for not only is seeding done from the air but also the topdressing with cobaltized superphosphate. The fertilizer is brought in by a fleet of trucks and stored in concrete bins holding upwards of a hundred tons. Within fifteen months of seeding, three dressings of fertilizer, each of 3 hundredweight to the acre (including 5 *ounces* of cobalt) are applied. On a 3,000-acre section this means 1,400 tons of phosphate. A minimum of fencing is also completed during the initial stage, sufficient to facilitate the concentration of the large numbers of livestock. Where surface water is lacking, deep wells are bored. Much of this work is done by contract; and the gangs of fencers and machinery operators either travel daily long distances to the job, or live in moveable hutments on the block. Before stock is turned out a minimum of housing for manager, shepherds and general hands is provided centrally on the block with the clearing of future sections in mind.

The phosphates promote a lush growth of clover and inaugurate the 'nitrogen cycle'. Hardy wethers, up to 7,000, are used to graze the new growth heavily in rotation, eating back not only the grass and clover but also volunteer fern and tutu. This process of chewing back all growth to the soil surface, of consolidating and dunging the soil, is repeated through summer and autumn. Wethers are followed – after the tutu, which is poisonous to cattle, is vanquished – by one-and two-year-old Aberdeen Angus steers. They, too, as many as 2,000 in the herd, are 'mob stocked'; and in the process do well on the thick growth of red clover which persists for four years, though it is gradually replaced by ryegrass, crested dogstail and white clover as fertility is built up with annual topdressings of phosphate and heavy stock manuring.

Two and a half years from the beginning of crushing, great rectangular sections of the tussock 'desert' or scrub 'moorland' – an untouched wilderness of drab greys and tawny yellows – have been converted into a smooth carpet of lush green broken only by a sparse network of new fence lines and raw, eroded pumice tracks. Alongside, other rectangles are being crushed or burned as the conversion is extended. On the new pastures dense concentrations of Romney ewes and black steers are 'working' and fulfilling their essential role as in-dispensable implements in the pioneering process. Close to the main access road there is a cluster of huts, a brand new house, machine sheds, fertilizer bin, piles of fenceposts and battens, coils of wire, and a battery of heavy machines.

During the stage of subsequent consolidation the dry stock are replaced – steers and wethers by wet ewes and breeding cows brought in from other development blocks where surpluses are now available. This stage is of variable duration, depending in part on how well stock and pastures do, on problems that may arise – stock diseases, soil erosion, etc. – and partly on the profitability of the 'station farming' programme. When the project is proven and major problems solved, and most if not all the costs of development recouped from livestock breeding, preparations are made for disposal to individual farmers. Internal fencing, houses, hay sheds, wool shed (or herring bone milking shed), sheep and cattle yards are erected and water reticulated to all paddocks without surface water. Electricity supply and necessary roading are completed and any land threatened by erosion is fenced off and reserved from grazing. The landscape begins to assume something of the ordinary appearance of an area of medium-size family farms except that all is new and raw. Weatherboard houses just painted are of a standard pattern, road metal is fresh, the corrugated iron walls and roof of the hay shed are still both unpainted and unrusted, the fence wire taut and the posts and battens are not weathered or coated with silver grey moss. The landscape is treeless, the pastures monotonously green and close cropped by stock, houses and buildings are exposed and not sheltered or shaded by trees, and the landscape is generally bleak and chill and raw.

Depending on the quality of the developed land and the ease of access to a dairy factory, subdivision is into sheep or dairy farms of a size sufficient (at the ruling prices paid for farm products) to ensure the purchaser of a reasonable income. With falls in farm incomes and the persistent rise in costs of operation new subdivisional units have over the years become larger in estimated stock carrying capacity and in acreage. Today 200 acre dairy farms (with a herd of over 100 cows plus replacements) and 500 acre sheep farms (carrying 1,800–2,000 ewe equivalents) are representative. These units are balloted to applicants approved as to their farm knowledge and experience and their ability, with the help of state loans, to finance the purchase of land and stock. Although the preference for returned servicemen long prevented others from entering ballots, most farms are today being allocated to civilians.

Gradually after disposal the farms and the rural landscape assume a maturity which approaches that of long settled farm areas, but without their endless variety of types of houses and farm buildings, of size of holdings and of intermixed land uses and farm economies. Farm houses sprout additional bedrooms, verandahs and TV aerials. Shelterbelts and shade trees are planted and grow rapidly. The outline of buildings is softened by the creation of domestic gardens. Live hedges are grown; battens weather and lose their regularity of spacing on sagging fence wires. Further internal subdivision takes place. Some farmers manage to increase carrying capacity and some introduce breeds and classes of livestock not included in those initially available from the land development agency. Some build up stud or recorded flocks of Romney, Border Leicester or Perendale sheep and of Jersey or Friesian cows. Slowly increasing maturity and diversity displace the raw freshness, the relative emptiness and the general uniformity of the landscape.

The tide of postwar land development has, to take one example, moved steadily south from the hydroelectric dams and settlements and new bridge crossings on the Waikato river at Mangakino and Maraetai to the northern shore of Lake Taupo. The construction of the new West Taupo highway from Te Awamutu to Tokaanu and Turangi has accompanied it. In 1948 hydroelectric power development on the Waikato river provided road access across the concrete dams to its left bank. The Mangapehu-Mangakino road was also built. This stimulated interest first in the 30,000 acre Pouakani block owned by Wairarapa Maoris. This was developed by the Department of Maori Affairs. By 1958 twenty-eight Maori dairy farmers had already been settled on 12,000 acres of new-won pastureland.

Between 1946 and 1965 the Crown acquired a total area of 35,700 acres alongside Pouakani – the Maraetai block, facing northwards and sloping down to the river. By 1950 the first farms were balloted to returned servicemen. Since then, but mainly in the late 1950s, a total of 120 farms, more than half of them dairy farms, have been taken up. They form an undulating to steep, rather monotonous, still treeless expanse of light green pastureland, more than 30,000 acres, rolling up from the southern shores of Whakamaru's long slender manmade lake. Mistakes were made here that are being remedied and avoided on later projects. The compaction of light pumice soils by mechanical rolling, and heavy stocking and the policy of close grazing have accelerated and concentrated run-off which is now cutting into the once vegetated bed and walls of natural drainageway in the pumice as into sugar, and presenting a formidable threat to the hydro-lakes and power generation. The Land Development Branch and the Waikato Valley Authority are repurchasing strips of land along and beside such eroding waterways, reserving them from grazing, and planting quick-growing strains of willows and poplars, incidentally adding a note of diversity and colour to the endless green of uninterrupted pastureland.

Fifteen years ago 1,250 ewe equivalents was a profitable number of livestock. On the Maraetai block this was estimated to require 350 acres. Although many farmers have subsequently stepped up the carrying capacity of their holdings, few have increased it sufficiently to carry the minimum of 1,800 ewe equivalents (and desirable 2,200) at 1968's prices for wool, lamb and skins. A few have surrendered their farms to the Land Settlement Board which has used them to enlarge the properties of more successful settlers. As a result of this experience the state is extending the period of consolidation and postponing subdivision on recently developed blocks. It is farming the large areas under 'station' conditions until the prices for farm products rise, or stabilize at lower levels and until the breakeven point is reached and the nation's capital investment in the costs of land development projects is fully recovered from farming profits.

South of the Maraetai block, over the gentle divide, and down to the shore of Lake Taupo, a distance of fifteen miles, is a compact series of blocks in a later stage of programmed development – Waipapa (Maori land), Tihoi, Puketapu, Marotiri, Acacia – and west of the lake, within the territory of the Te Kuiti office of the Land Development Branch – Waihaha, Waikino, Whareroa (Maori land) and Te Hapua. Much of this land was only a decade ago so isolated, remote and untenanted as to be ideal for use as a military training ground. Here today a total of almost 100,000 acres is in process of clearing and grassing and consolidation or in the very early stages of individual settlement. Because some sections are still occupied by tussock, especially the 'frost flats', stunted manuka, tall scrub or second growth forest, others bare and black following a successful recent burn, others lush with the red clover's vigorous response to phosphate, still others closely grazed by heavily stocked steers and wethers, and some green and virgin and just taken over by successful ballotees, there is a temporary variety of scene – a variety that changes bewilderingly between even annual visits.

South of the lake, adjacent to the Taupo-Napier highway, where the head-waters of the Rangitaiki and Mohaka come together on either side of an indefinite rolling divide with frosty terraces and valley flats and the sparsest of scrub and tussock vegetation, are blocks of land silently awaiting development – as yet trodden only by feral goats, deer and horses. Here are the 42,000 acres of the Whakatau block. Here, too, is Lochinver, recently tackled by a private developer, an urban highway contractor and philanthropist. Already he has created emerald green islands in the drab and featureless extent of the plateau. Miles back from the highway bright green low hills rise above grey desertlike flats – the outcome of the use of private capital and enterprise, of aerial top-dressing and of heavy machine operations. On the clover-covered flat at the foot of the improved hill slopes is a grassed airstrip almost two miles in length. Today the main problem on Lochinver, where sixty years ago Cheviot sheep scratched for a time a miserable existence and died in large numbers from 'bush sickness' and lack of winter feed, is to breed stock fast enough to provide adequate and heavy enough grazing of the rich growth of pastures being won from the empty wilderness.

Incidental reference has already been made to the other spectacular additions to the landscapes of the North Island interior and to their important contribution to the economy of the whole of the North Island. From the flow of the Waikato river within the limits of the plateau, regulated and reinforced by the storage capacity of Lake Taupo, and from the frightening pressurized reservoir of geothermal steam, heat and energy that drilling has revealed at Wairakei a few miles from Taupo and close to the Waikato, and at Kawerau, there has been harnessed almost a million kilowatts of electric power. From Taupo downstream, the river has been converted into a succession of stepped lakes. The riser of each step is in the form of a massive geometrically curved concrete dam with its powerhouse and adjacent 'hydro village'. Until Benmore on the Waitaki came into operation in 1965, seven such hydroelectric power stations strung along the thread of the Waikato accounted for almost half of all the water power harnessed in the whole country. But the Waikato's potential is now largely tapped. Only by elaborate engineering in the headwaters of the streams supplying Lake Taupo, and only by enlarging their catchments and artificially capturing through tunnels, canals and aquaducts some headwater streams of the Wanganui and Maowhango which drain the northern and southern slopes of Ruapehu in the Tongariro National Park, is the generation of the existing stations on the Waikato to be enlarged and a new station constructed at Tokaanu. This programme of construction will give rise to yet another new town on the plateau – at Turangi. Not only will it accommodate the men working on the scheme and their families, but it is also planned to be a permanent urban centre of 8,000 or 10,000 persons based ultimately on forestry, farming and the holiday and recreational business as well as on power. In addition it will almost certainly become the service centre for the extensive scrubland still to be won for farms between Taupo and Mangakino, much of which is close to the West Taupo highway which runs south to Turangi and links there with State Highway No. 1.

Most unusual of all the Volcanic Plateau's long unsuspected resources is its geothermal heat and steam. The heat of the earth's interior can only be utilized where the crust is thin and water is present so that the heat is carried by steam or hot water in hydrothermal fields. Such is the case over much of the plateau. At Rotorua and elsewhere hot water and steam, occurring naturally at the surface, have long been used for their curative properties, for heating swimming baths and private pools, for domestic central heating of homes, for drying timber, warming glasshouses and growing mushrooms.

But since 1949 the undulating scrub covered landscape at Wairakei, interspersed with clumps of volunteer radiata pines, has been drastically changed. In place of the thin wisps of hissing steam among the manuka there are today massive, snorting white clouds and powerful roaring jets rising into the clear air high above the tall pines. They issue from vertical concrete towers fitted with bell-mouthed silencers which fail to stifle the train-like hiss and rumble of steam. There is a maze of giant, parallel assemblages of heavy pipes. They convey steam and water separately under the main highway and down to the riverside powerhouse where this bonus of the region's volcanic oddities and attractions provides an electric power capacity of 192,420 kW. The locality has also become a tourist attraction, bizarre and unique, awesome and noisy compared with the older power dams and hydro-lakes in the vicinity.

Scientists and engineers suggest that the exploitation of geothermal energy is merely in the infant exploratory stage that the petroleum industry reached half a century ago. Petroleum is now discovered and extracted from what only

13. *Volcanic Plateau: Wairakei geothermal power project*
This aerial view gives but a subdued impression of the tremendous power and frightening roar of the steam bores. Most of the steam is carried away in pipes and its energy harnessed at a power station beside the Waikato river. Notice also the private plantings of pine and the plateau-like form of the landscape.

two decades ago were considered totally impossible depths, locations and strata. It may be the same with geothermal heat. It has already been seriously estimated that the Volcanic Plateau's geothermal steam could support indefinitely a generating capacity of a million kilowatts; and the authoritative suggestion has been made that within twenty years its energy production could exceed today's North Island output from all other sources. Even when its land has been fully planted to timber trees or converted into farms, there could still be exciting and spectacular changes in the landscapes of the Volcanic Plateau for New Zealanders.

Meanwhile development proceeds apace. What a generation ago was still a remote, distant, sparsely occupied and unpromising pioneer fringe, is now a hub of activity, of economic progress, of dynamic change, of expanding production and of moderately dense rural settlement by New Zealand standards.

Indeed New Zealanders claim it is becoming overcrowded at the height of the holiday season, and its main tar-sealed lakeside roads uncomfortably clogged with traffic. The beaches and holiday homes that rim the shores of lakes, the yachts and launches on their surface, the echelons of fly fishermen that wade the shallow lake waters and frequently land 5–10 pound rainbow and brown trout, the campers and bathers, the coloured jungle of tents and caravans, the lakeside traffic jams, the cafés and curio shops – all bear witness to the seasonal flow of holidaymakers, to its increasing volume and to the demand for ever better communications and improved access.

The forests are now being harvested and almost everywhere rapid natural regeneration of pines follows felling. The orderly blocks of tall dark pines are interrupted increasingly by clear-felled sections where disorder and disarray are the keynotes to the scene, as if a tropical Pacific hurricane had recently passed this way and flattened all in its track. Broken and maimed logs, a tangle of bark, branches and waste timber litter the surface – red and brown and

14. *Volcanic Plateau: Kawerau*
To handle the harvest of quick-growing softwoods, transport facilities, townships and industrial plant have had to be constructed and people brought to the plateau. This is the Tasman Pulp and Paper Company's integrated newsprint, woodpulp and sawmill beside the new special settlement built at Kawerau.

ragged. The piercing warning shouts of the timber workers, the harsh whistle of the crane and dragline, the buzz of power saws, the roar of bulldozers, the rumble of the twenty-two tyres of articulated logging trucks and trailers on pumice roads, the heat, dust, bustle and pinewood-spiced air alternate with the cool shade and stillness and the silent browsing of deer in the deep, dark interior of the hushed battalions of standing trees.

The timber workers, heavy machine operators and truck drivers are predominantly Maoris, as are the workers on the land development contracts. They live temporarily on or close to the job, returning for the weekend to their traditional villages elsewhere on the plateau, in the Urewera country and on the Bay of Plenty coast or, more often these days, to their modern state or Maori Affairs Department bungalow homes in Taupo, Rotorua or Whakatane. After Auckland, Rotorua has New Zealand's largest urban agglomeration of Maori people.

Maori women play an important role in the expanding tourist and holiday trade. In Rotorua's hotels and motels, in its shops and cafés, young Maori women monopolize employment in domestic service. Rotorua is thus not only an important administrative centre of land development but also of Maori affairs.

Long isolated, neglected, shunned, the North Island interior today bustles with life and change. In two decades between the 1945 and 1966 censuses, the population of Rotorua and Taupo counties, including the urban population within them, has expanded from 18,808 to 60,887 – a percentage increase of 224 against a total growth of national population in the same period of 57 per cent. Rotorua borough has become Rotorua city and the urban area population has expanded to almost four times its population at the end of World War II.

But the growth of human population has not kept pace with that of domestic livestock nor the rate of transformation of the plateau's once unattractive acres. Whilst the number of holdings has almost trebled, the extent of the land and landscape in 'grass, clovers and lucerne' has quadrupled in twenty years and now totals half a million acres. Most spectacular statistics, however, are those referring to livestock. The livestock population of Rotorua and Taupo counties, measured in ewe equivalents, has expanded fivefold. Before the war the Volcanic Plateau could be classed as a 'non-agricultural' area. Today it has a heavy livestock population and its farms are among the country's most modern, efficient and progressive. It has indeed as many livestock units or ewe equivalents in relation to population as the country as a whole. It contributes its share of the nation's agricultural exports, the bulk of New Zealand's internal requirements of timber products and almost all its exports of pulp, paper and logs; and its hydro and geothermal power motivate most of the North Island's factories, drive its milking machines and shearing plant, light its homes and streets, heat its water and cook its meals. In addition, the Volcanic Plateau is a pleasant holiday retreat with a unique assortment of attractions.

Chapter 8
Farm landscapes

New Zealand's is still largely a 'colonial' economy. Its agriculture, predominantly pastoral, provides 94 per cent of the value of the nation's exports. And trading is the country's lifeblood. On a *per capita* basis it has long conducted a volume of international trade as great as that of any nation. For some decades the *per capita* value of its imports and exports far exceeded that of any other country. Only since 1938, with largely forlorn attempts to reduce its importing propensity by fostering manufacturing industries and by strict licensing of imports and foreign exchange transactions, has it had to share primacy in the *per capita* amount and value of its international trading with some of the small nations of Europe, or to yield it to one or two new-rich oil states in the Middle East.

Gross farming income amounted in the 1967–68 season to $826 million,* of which two-thirds arose from the export of farm produce. A growing proportion, now more than a third, is consumed in New Zealand by a population of 2·78 million people. To man New Zealand's 68,000 farms requires fewer than 117,500 persons – most of them independent farmers and only a third of them farm labourers, shepherds, shearers, milkers, fencers and farm contractors. This is only 11·6 of the country's labour force, totalling in October 1967 just over a million persons.

The 68,000 farms, slowly declining in number but increasing in average size and in the scale of operation, occupy almost 43·5 million acres, which is almost two-thirds of the total area of the country. Of the total number of operational holdings, 1,000 are on the Volcanic Plateau and 400 in the South Island high country. In these particular cases, 'station' is often to be preferred to 'farm'. In the former area the development of more than a million acres for farming is recent, and has not as yet produced mature rural landscapes or firm-rooted farm economies. In the latter a century's occupance of 13 million acres of tussock grassland has made relatively little visual impression on the natural landscape.

The remaining 30 million acres of occupied farm land and approximately 66,500 farm units are the subject of investigation in this chapter. Almost half the country is involved; and its farm landscapes are regionally diverse in

---

* Since 1965–66 the *value* of total farm production has fallen by more than $26 millions although the volume of farm output has risen by 7 per cent.

character despite the overwhelming prevalence of pastoral forms of agriculture and of livestock rearing economies.

The process of converting a sharply varying, predominantly rugged and forested 'natural' terrain into mature, or fast-maturing, humanized agricultural landscapes is the real history of New Zealand in the 125 years of its European settlement. The extent, completeness and success of this transformation is the very basis of New Zealand's economy and of the progress, prosperity and trade of its people. The wholesale conversion of the wild and pristine landscape was precipitate, violent, and quickly over. It had its dangers, disasters and disappointments. It was accomplished by a mere handful of people and largely within a century. It is an exciting – even frightening – story. Only a few years ago, and in many areas, its success was not assured until, as the ultimate frontier was approached, improved techniques were devised and modern science was drawn on to consolidate and complete the transformation.

Now the future wellbeing and preservation of the settled and productive rural landscapes will require not physical effort, brute force, tears and toil or even powerful machines, but sophisticated economic, political and social planning at both the national and international levels. Failure to devise formulae and institutions that enable efficiently produced foodstuffs, fibres and animal proteins to reach the empty bellies and to cover the bare backs of the millions of human beings who require them could still readily speed New Zealand's extensively but expertly utilized farm landscapes on a course of rapid reversion. It could well result in the early occupation of much hill country by a vigorous indigenous scrub and forest vegetation – a vegetation which still presents a threat and which is capable of obliterating most of the alien flora Europeans have assembled and subsequently tended.

New Zealand agriculture and the rural landscapes that farming activities have so largely moulded are young. But farm practice has progressed rapidly in technology, efficiency and output. There are hundreds of farms and entire agricultural regions which, two generations ago, were in scrub, swamp or bush and much as they had been for centuries before, but which today are rarely equalled in the world in terms of the quality and carrying capacity of their pastures and the expert efficiency and *per capita* productivity of their livestock farming. Some agricultural areas are still in the process of conversion and development; and much hill country, ruthlessly cleared of bush and soon to be as quickly abandoned in the 1930s, is only now, with the widespread use of aerial topdressing and oversowing, being brought into economic production.

The one outstandingly important crop in New Zealand is grass. The pervading colour of the farm landscape is a year-round bright green. Arable agriculture is relatively insignificant – either in the national economy or the rural scene. Livestock products account for 86 per cent of gross farm income: grain and field crops, orchards, market gardens, poultry, bee-keeping and all other intensive forms of agriculture are responsible together for only 14 per cent of the farmer's income; they may well come into greater prominence, however, in the next generation.

The basic role of New Zealand farms since the 1880s, which brought the introduction of refrigerated transport of perishable commodities, has been to produce a massive surplus of protein-rich livestock products for disposal in markets half the world away. It is based on the grazing of sheep and cattle of different breeds on native ranges, but more especially on lush alien pasture grasses and clovers, and on techniques evolved in New Zealand for establishing, maintaining and constantly improving pasture swards. It is, above all, the techniques and patterns of farm management devised to fit the sharply varying regional combination of conditions – but generally involving naturally infertile soils, mild winters, abundant rainfall and generous amounts of sunshine – that have enabled the New Zealand farmer to outstrip all his counterparts in the world in *per capita* productivity, and to see his production sold profitably in discriminating markets despite the distance and transport costs involved.

While the average size of farms, including the large high country stations, is 635 acres – and is increasing significantly – the farms which occupy the productive plains, downland and hill country average little over 400 acres in size. Holdings between 100 and 650 acres form 60 per cent of all farms. They occupy less than a quarter of all the land in farms, but more than half of the 'cultivated' or improved land. Of 22·2 million acres of cultivated land, 19·8 million (a figure which has risen since 1960 by 1·5 million acres) are in sown grasses, that is, are permanent pastureland of divergent quality, botanical composition and stock carrying capacity. Only a million acres of farmland are in crops, a million acres in farm plantations, windbreaks and woodlots of exotic conifers and broadleafed trees, and 32,000 acres under intensive cultivation and in market-garden, nursery or orchard crops. It is these 22·2 million acres of cultivated land and the as yet unused and unimproved bush, scrub and swamp on farms that provide the variegated, but prevailingly grass-green, rural landscapes of New Zealand and which, from the air, appear to be crawling, swarming and alive with flocks and herds of domestic animals.

In 1969 there were 8·6 million cattle, 2·2 million of them dairy cows in milk and 1·5 million beef breeding cows. At the same time (though the number fluctuates markedly through the season) there were 63 million sheep, including 43 million breeding ewes expected to produce a little over 100 per cent of lambs in the three months from August on.

Converted to 'livestock units' (which, according to New Zealand practice, are termed 'ewe equivalents'), the domestic farm livestock population in the latter part of 1969 (spring) is no less than the equivalent of 142 million ewes – a flock of fifty to every man, woman and child, both Maori and *pakeha*, living in New Zealand at the time, including the 70 per cent of the population living and working in towns. No other country has such a density of farm livestock. Taking all farm units – not excluding those in which livestock play no part – there are more than 2,000 livestock units to every farm. No other people depend so completely on sheep and cattle. No other rural landscapes are so intimately designed for, or contoured, shaped and moulded by, the farmers' grazing animals.

Dairy farm landscapes

On New Zealand farms there are fewer herds of dairy cows than flocks of sheep. But the number of farms classed as predominantly dairy farms (26,000) is as large as the number of holdings on which sheep provide clearly the principal source of income. At the same time the average size of farms listed as 'predominantly dairy' (147 acres) is only one-eighth the average size of sheep farms. These simple statistics emphasize and partly explain two other facts. Dairying is more often a markedly specialized form of livestock farming than is sheep rearing. It occurs in smaller units over a much more restricted total area than sheep farming and is indeed concentrated in small pockets of rich lowland pastures where there is less variation in size of units, farm economy, systems of stock and pasture management, and in the rural scene and landscape, than is the case in those areas where sheep are the principal source of income.

Specialized intensive dairy farming, for which New Zealand agriculture is perhaps best known in the world, is largely confined to the North Island. Although its origins in the 1880s, when it first became possible to ship butter as refrigerated cargo, may be traced to the South Island and to Southland in particular, the South Island today produces liquid milk and processed dairy products mainly for domestic consumption and contributes little to the massive export trade in butter, cheese and dried milk powders.

Intensive dairy farming was, and still is, more appropriate to the North Island. With the ending of the Maori Wars in the 1870s, the development of refrigeration in the 1880s, the tying up of land in the South Island in large parcels, and the demand of South Island farm labourers and urban unemployed for access to the land, a movement north began in the last quarter of the century. The reliable rains and the mildness of the winter half-year in the North Island were better for dairying than the markedly seasonal pasture growth, dry summers and sharp winter frosts of leeward South Island localities. First the damp coastal forest and scrub lands were made available in small lots. It was initially as much as a man could handle to clear from 50 to 100 acres of dense forest and put the land in grass.

Milk and its derivatives produced a steady, regular and immediate return. Shorthorn cattle were grazed amidst the fallen charred logs and tall black stumps on the lush cocksfoot and clovers sown on soils fertilized with the ash of the forest burn, especially on the mild rainy coast from the Horowhenua to Mount

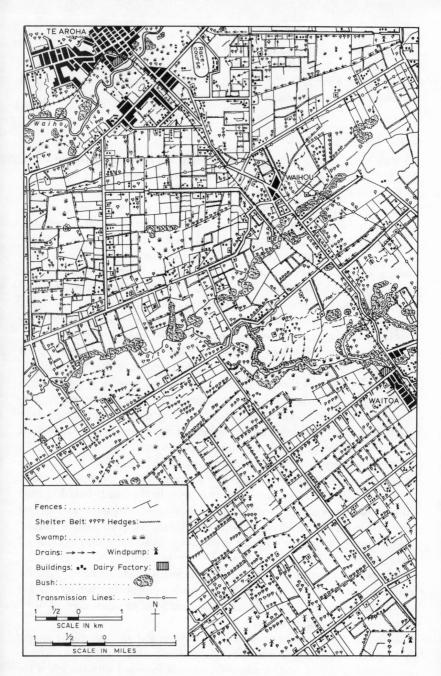

15. *Waikato dairy farm landscape*

Egmont where, at Urenui, difficult hill country ran out to the littoral and faced directly the Tasman breakers. From their tiny bush farms these pioneer dairymen carted wholemilk by dray over clay tracks to the quickly erected local creamery for separation. There was a limit to the time and so also to the length of this journey. The cooperative creameries were thus built at five, six or seven mile intervals and beside them there was established the nucleus of a township. Taranaki is the oldest of the Dominion's specialized dairy lands. Its tradition of wholemilk collection early gave it dominance in cheese production – a dominance which persists today.

The lowland swamps and alluvial flats of the Hauraki plains and Waikato-Waipa valley turned to dairying a generation later. First, difficult and elaborate land drainage and reclamation were necessary. Only the government could organize such essential development. By then the hand-operated home separator was in use, roads were metalled and the motor vehicle in its infant years. Cream, rather than bulkier loads of wholemilk, was collected by motor lorry from the cream stand each farmer erected at his gate beside the road. In this case the dairy factories and the small towns that grew around them, or in which they were built, are twelve to twenty miles apart, and the towns have grown larger than in Taranaki. These newer dairy lands produced butter almost exclusively until tanker collection of wholemilk led in recent years to increased processing of wholemilk and skimmed milk powders and casein.

Subsequently dairy farming extended into the Bay of Plenty and south to the Rangitaiki plains; and most recently, with the roading of the 'roadless' (and 'winterless') north, it has spread discontinuously into Northland and is also presently pioneering parts of the inland pumice plateau. Wherever intensive commercial dairy farming is found today the land is flat, near-flat or easily undulating and generally of low elevation. Rarely does it climb the hills. In all cases the climate is mild and rainfall adequate except for occasional erratic (usually late summer) dry spells – 'drought' is everywhere too strong a word. These dry spells steepen the autumn decline in butterfat production or terminate the milking season somewhat prematurely. Rarely is the soil inherently fertile. Its fertility is typically manmade. Taranaki has advantages in that it is least prone to dry spells and its friable yellow-brown loams, derived from Egmont volcanic ash, are more fertile and physically more manageable than either the heavier clays or gley soils of the Hauraki and the north, or than the lighter pumice soils of the Bay of Plenty and the rim of the Volcanic Plateau. No other dairy region is quite so specialized. In no other do cows in milk form such a high proportion of all livestock units.

When compared with sheep and beef cattle, the distribution of dairy cows reveals a pattern of sharp concentration rather than of general dispersion. Nine out of ten are in the North Island, six out of ten north of an irregular line across the North Island between Te Kuiti and Opotiki. The major pockets of concen-

16. *Southern Waikato: Te Awamutu dairy farm landscape*
This 104 acre, all-grass farm carries 94 cows in milk and replacements by judicious
rotational grazing of 22 small, wire-fenced or barberry-hedged fields. Notice the 'race'
providing access to all enclosures.

tration of dairy cows and 'cow cockies' are, in order of size and significance:
the Hauraki plains and the ash-covered low downland in the middle Piako and
Waihou valleys; the ring of gently undulating lowland around the base of
Mount Egmont, with coastal fingers reaching northeast to Urenui and southeast
to Patea; and the middle basin of the Waikato and the Waipa valley. With the
rural areas immediately south of the Auckland urban area, where the emphasis
is on town milk supply, and the Bay of Plenty littoral, the Waikato and Hauraki-
Piako lowlands constitute the green heart of the New Zealand dairy farming
industry with almost half of all the country's cows in milk. Lesser concentrations
are found in Northland especially on the Ruawai flats, on the Manawatu plain,
in the Bush District (Pahiatua, Woodville, Dannevirke) east of the ranges, and
in the Wairarapa. In the South Island the two largest concentrations of dairy

farming are in Southland (on the inland fringe of the Awarua swamp east of Invercargill) and immediately northeast and southwest of Christchurch. Neither has as many dairy cattle as any of the North Island pockets named and both are increasingly concerned with supplying adjacent urban areas with their daily liquid milk requirements.

It is impossible here to describe adequately all the pocketed dairy farming landscapes. The broad uniformity of their cultural elements makes this, however, less necessary. Yet their physical settings may vary and the lesser details of farm practice make for interesting variety from region to region in minor features of the rural landscape. The dairylands described here are some of those that make up what earlier was referred to as the 'green heart of the New Zealand dairy farming industry' – between Auckland and Opotiki and Auckland and Te Kuiti.

It is the vivid all-year-round emerald green of the small pasture enclosures on which concentrations of Friesian herds, totalling from 70 to 150 cows, are rotationally grazed in the immediate vicinity of the Auckland International Airport that create a lasting impression on first-time visitors to the country. Travelling south from Auckland one enters the northernmost extension of the green heart of dairying before the urban motorway gives way to the Great South Road, twenty-five miles from Queen Street. It is a frequent experience for the speeding motorist to catch a flashing glimpse of a string of black-and-white cows strolling leisurely in line ahead across the new concrete bridges that straddle the motorway and link the separate parts of farms cut in two by the rumbling traffic artery. Dairying dominates the rural parts of the landscape at East Tamaki, in the Papakura-Clevedon fault trough, in and out between the farflung residential suburbs and new industrial factory sites between Papatoetoe, Wiri, Manurewa and Papakura, over the gently rolling slopes of the Karaka whose friable ash soils reach westwards to the 500 feet high stabilized dunes extending from the Waikato mouth to the Manukau Heads, around the base of the gently inclined volcanic slopes of Pukekohe Hill crowded with the intensively cultivated plots of market gardeners, into the Pokeno valley and around the waterlogged margins of the Maramarua swamp. All these districts lie within Manukau City and Franklin County where there are no less than 180,000 dairy cows and a variety of other stock. They graze 330,000 acres of rich ryegrass-paspalum-white clover pastures (kept 4 to 6 inches long by careful grazing management), and produce, with the help of silage and hay saved in November and December and fed out in June, July and August, a steady flow of milk the year round for pasteurization in city treatment plants and retailing in bottles to metropolitan householders.

Here farms are generally small and land values high. The imminence of urban expansion, the land's potential for urban use, soaring local body rates, and the advantages of closeness to urban markets, milk treatment plants and abattoirs force farm land prices to well over $500 an acre. Livestock are numerous. A 100-acre dairy farm may well milk a changing cow population, totalling in excess of 100 at all times throughout the year. Some town milk-supply farms are larger; some twice as large. A number are quite small, less efficient, untidy and not so up-to-date. Sometimes replacements are not bred on the farm, although most outer suburban dairy farmers make maximum use of artificial insemination services, obviating the need for buying and feeding bulls but ensuring the production of high yielding heifer replacements. Their special and peculiar problem is to have cows calving at intervals through the year and to maintain feed supplies and the flow of milk (in accordance with the quota set) through the cooler months when grass growth is slowed and when heavy treading of damp pastures pugs the ground and further reduces pasture growth.

The gently rolling landscape is intensely, but irregularly, subdivided by permanent fences and still further temporarily subdivided for rationed and rotational grazing by moveable single-wire electric fences. Many hawthorn, gorse and other English shrub hedges, planted when, after the Maori wars, settlement first moved cautiously south in the 1870s from the soldier settlement outposts of Onehunga, Panmure and Howick, have recently been bulldozed away; and scattered clumps or single specimens of early planted giant macrocarpas, radiata pines and eucalypts have been felled to make way for more pasture. The countryside still has an open wooded appearance, but it is a mature, tidy, colourful landscape, thickly settled. There are older wooden houses, small and cosy, roofed with corrugated iron, and immediately alongside them very often a trim, architect-designed, modern brick or concrete block home with large glassed picture windows as if removed from a fashionable city suburb. Close by are the sparklingly clean, grey, concrete yards and new-built herring-bone* milking shed, the refrigerated stainless steel milk vat housed in the end of the shed, and the metalled turning circle used by the articulated milk tanker when it collects the milk each day. Concrete races connect most enclosures with the shed and along these the herd makes its leisurely way twice daily, rain or shine, to the shed and back. There is a large hay barn and possibly a silage stack. Supplementary supplies of hay may well be bought-in each summer. Some dairy men own or lease hilly run-offs in the Hunua ranges to the east or on the dunes of coarse sand along the Awhitu peninsula where they graze heifers, dry

---

* The electrically operated herring-bone milking shed, constructed of concrete and with railings of galvanized piping, has a central pit in which the dairyman operates, changing the pulsating milking cups. The pit is the central feature of the shed and the herring-bone. The cows are forced to stand at an angle with their rear quarters to the pit and their udders within easy reach and at a suitable working height for the men working in the pit. With a herring-bone shed one man can handle in the same time 20 per cent more cows. Farms which were formerly uneconomic have become economic for one-man operation with the erection in the last five years of a herring-bone shed. The herring-bone has replaced the walk-through shed, built of timber with stalls in which the cows stood side by side. The farmer operated on the same level with much bending and walking and slower operation. It was at once less hygienic and less efficient.

cows or cows close to calving, and so are able to lift the population of milking cows on the home farm and maintain during winter months their individual gallonage of milk production rigidly fixed by quota.

Others prefer to ensure maximum utilization of the spring and early summer flush of growth by temporarily taking on additional livestock at that season rather than by increasing the number of cows in milk to be fed during the following winter. They may buy ewes with lambs at foot in August and September, or early-weaned store lambs in November, or forward yearling Aberdeen Angus or Hereford steers, fattening and disposing of them profitably before the autumn slows pasture growth. This is made more convenient and profitable as a result of the closeness of livestock auction markets at Pukekohe, Tuakau and Papakura and of the city fatstock saleyards and export meat freezing works and municipal abattoirs alongside at Westfield. Distances are short, stock carriers always at hand and freight charges low. In summer, then, the small lush green enclosures are thickly dotted with varied concentrations of livestock: sleek herds of Friesian cows; compact black beef steers; stocky Southdown-Romney cross lambs; slim, dappled black-and-white heifer calves; and here and there, on separate properties of small acreage, are huddled sties with squealing porkers, ever hungry for the city and factory waste on which they are fed; and long batteries housing thousands of laying hens. Within the region, too, and especially at Takanini, racehorses are bred and trained on small properties most of which however have their miniature oval earth training tracks.

Along the roads, past the farm gates, traffic is heavy, especially at weekends when city folk seek relief from their urban environment and Sunday lawn-mowing chores by motoring through the sparkling rural landscape, or by hurrying to sun-drenched beaches. Through the middle of the intensively used, densely occupied pastoral countryside cuts the broad swathe of the motorway with the hushed purr maintained by the processions of speeding vehicles; and overhead giant jets appear scarcely to move as they circle noisily to approach Auckland International airport's massive 8,000 feet of concrete landing.

If you turn left at the foot of the Bombay hills and follow the tip of the southern spurs of the Hunua ranges you soon reach Waitakururu at the southwestern corner of the Firth of Thames. Here, abruptly, you move into a strikingly different agricultural landscape, where dairy cows, to the virtual exclusion of other classes of livestock, are even more prominent than in South Auckland. And the land is flat or near-flat. This is the Hauraki plain, laid down in the Firth of Thames principally by the Waikato river when, at the time of the major Taupo eruptions, its suspended load of pumice was thick and choking. Later the Waikato was diverted again to the northwest through where Cambridge and Hamilton now stand to discharge on the west coast into the Tasman Sea. The Waikato left a broad swampy flat built in the main of redistributed pumice. This has since been extended into the firth by the alluvial deposition of the embanked and meandering Piako and Waihou rivers and by marine sedimentation. A third of the Hauraki plain is still a dismal expanse of grey-brown swamp, its raupo, rushes, sedges and stunted manuka the haunt of the waterfowl and a favourite retreat for duck shooters. Here and there are forlorn remnants of the kahikatea forest that once attracted the attention of Captain Cook as a source of spars and was later used to furnish millions of butter boxes. Most of the plain, however, either stands a little above winter flood level or has since 1907 been artificially drained by a network of deep-cut main and shallower subsidiary channels and river cuts, and has been protected by embankments.

From Waitakururu to Paeroa, diagonally across the plains, the main road follows the accordant rectangular pattern of artificial drainage, property boundaries and internal farm subdivision by frequent abrupt right-angled turns except where, as at Netherton, it mounts the 10-foot high stopbank of the Waihou river and meanders for a while alongside the river, providing one of the few uninterrupted views over a portion of the plain eastwards to the dark fault wall of the Coromandel range, westward to the low green downland beyond Kaihere and Patetonga. Elsewhere the view is restricted by the dense shelterbelts and hedges of pampas grass that the pioneer dairy farmers planted to provide shade and shelter, or to fill a gap between deep drain and property boundary. *Cupressus lawsoniana*, with its heavy drooping dark olive-green foliage down to ground level, is the favourite and effective shelter tree. It was mainly planted not more than forty-five years ago. Most farmhouses and farm buildings are of this age too. Nor have they been as frequently replaced or supplemented by modern homes as in parts of the Waikato and South Auckland or the longer settled dairy region of Taranaki. This may be partly due to the initial regularly small size of farms (from 60 to 100 acres) and the severe – though high – limit to carrying capacity and production set by winter waterlogging and pugging of pastures. Soils are meadow soils and organic soils, initially as fertile as most in New Zealand. But even more effective and more extensive artificial drainage is required not only to create additional farmland from the hitherto unmolested peat swamps but to raise the productivity of existing farms.

The tarsealed road bumps its way over the drained and shrinking peat paralleled by deep drains. Access to the farms which stand a little back from the road is past the roadside letterbox and old cream stand, and over the main drain by a wooden bridge. Beyond the house and buildings and the garden and shelter trees around them, the landscape opens up. The damp pastures of paspalum, ryegrass, Yorkshire fog and legumes, pugged in winter and as a result sometimes invaded in summer by buttercup and pennyroyal except where hormone sprays are used, reach back on either side of a central concrete race. Shallow drains parallel the wire fences or pampas grass hedges. Fencing on deep peat is difficult. Posts have poor holding and can be pushed over by cattle. Where loose wire fences are not bordered by drains the farmer may run a temporary electrified wire a foot or two in front of the inadequate permanent fence. Heavy crops of hay are taken in December, but for the rest of the milking season – 260 days from early August to April – the herd of sixty to ninety cows is rotated over the 5-acre enclosures.

The herd here is of Jerseys – cream and buff and charcoal in colour, slim and slight in conformation, but capable of producing more butterfat per acre than any other breed. In Hauraki Plains county, with its 104,000 acres of grassland and 700 farms, there are almost 100,000 dairy cows. The proportion of cows in milk to total cattle (58 : 100) and the proportion of total cattle to sheep shorn (161 : 100) are higher than in any other administrative county in the green heart of dairying and exceeded only in one small county in Taranaki (Waimate West).

South of the swamp wilderness that fills the lower central part of the graben occupied by the Waihou and Piako rivers you enter Piako and Matamata counties. Here elevation is greater, natural drainage more effective and, further south, you rise on to shallow alluvial terraces and the gentle slopes of downland and hills cut into the northernmost terminal of the Volcanic Plateau's ignimbrite sheet. The landscape opens up and the view becomes more expansive with the variation in slope. This is the epitome of New Zealand commercial dairy farming landscapes.

The two counties have 420,000 dairy cows. They also have 85,000 beef cattle and a fast-growing number of young 'dairy beef' cattle – Friesian and crossbred Jersey steers being reared for beef production. But they also have almost a million sheep, three-quarters of them on the hillier slopes of Matamata county, especially on the basal slopes of the Kaimai and Mamaku ranges, but many of them on dairy farms. Farms are a little more extensive, averaging 260 acres in the two counties. The larger farms on the slopes beyond Tirau and Putaruru have remnant patches of bush and scrub in the deeper gullies. Some of the smaller farms north of Waitoa and Waihou still have undrained, little-used margins of swamp and peat with an open scatter of the conical form of relict kahikatea and the palm-like shape of cabbage trees, their feet in water. On the downs and drier terraces of coarse, watersorted pumice, fodder crops may be grown – swedes, turnips, chou mollier. One acre of pasture in five or six is cut for hay or ensilage. For every farm there are 170 cattle of all kinds and 300 sheep (together with 230 lambs tailed each spring). This represents approximately five livestock units (or ewe equivalents) to every acre in farms, or over six to every acre of grass and clover. In brief, the flats, easy slopes and steep valley sides of Piako and Matamata counties are more heavily populated with domestic farm livestock than any similarly extensive area in New Zealand, and probably in the world. Their small, irregularly fenced, crisp, close-cropped, copious green pastures swarm with a variety of sheep and cattle, but more particularly with Jersey cows and Romney ewes.

The landscape varies, but not the heavy livestock carrying capacity. East of

Morrinsville the near-flat plain has an irregular grid of straight roads, narrow but sealed. Artificial drains, farm boundaries and the small fenced fields are also irregularly rectangular. Clumps of trees, a cluster of buildings composed of a tidy modern farmhouse and an older smaller residence housing farm labourer or sharemilker, a new concrete herring-bone cowbail and sterilized dairy, the metalled turning circle, and hay and implement sheds, mark the close-set frequency and indicate the relative smallness of farms. Here they average between 100 and 150 acres. But as the ground rises to the south, larger farms – up to 500 or 600 acres – have paddocks of all shapes and sizes, and a pattern of fences adjusted to variable terrain and slope. The bright green of short pastures where the ewes and lambs graze is relieved by the tall dark green of a hay crop as it awaits the mower and baling machine, its ryegrass seedheads alternately glistening silver and russety-purple as they are buffeted in the wind, or by an occasional rare patch of cultivation – the fresh green of young maize or the light red-brown of the soil where last year's crop of chou mollier stood. In some gullies are the grey and silver of flowering manuka or the riotous golden bloom of rampant gorse. There are fences of wire and live hedges of barberry, box-thorn and gorse, and in every direction clumps, or belts, of trees – eucalypts, radiata pines, macrocarpa and Lawson's cypress, and tall Lombardy poplars and plane trees which, with the first frost in May, give the landscape its splashes of autumn tints and splendour as the cows are dried-off and the first bales of hay carted out.

Although dairying is supreme, the farm economy is usually based on mixed livestock farming. The supremacy of butterfat is reflected not only in the frequency of older butter factories but also in the massive modern dairy factories – among the largest in New Zealand and in the world – at Waitoa, Waharoa, Morrinsville (2), and the fleet of milk tankers that pound the country roads. But the mixed livestock economy is seen in the fact that, once off the flat, woolsheds are as numerous as cowbails, and both often occur on the same property. Alongside the sheepyards are other stouter yards for beef cattle, and beside the road is a loading dock designed for the quick and efficient despatch to the freezing works not only of boner dairy cows, but also of fat steers, fat lambs and cast-for-age ewes. There may be several corrugated iron hay barns both close to the farmstead and at a distance. Although both herd and flock replacements may be reared on the larger farms, the southern Waihou-Piako valley is, like the Waikato-Waipa valley, a market for the store sheep and beef cattle breeder of the Poverty Bay-East Coast hill country, the King Country, the Raglan-Kawhia hills and the Coromandel peninsula. Weaner crossbred Hereford-Angus cattle, store sheep and cast-for-age ewes sold at autumn livestock fairs come here for wintering, the cattle and lambs for fattening and finishing, the ewes to be mated to Southdown, South Dorset and Suffolk rams and to produce another crop of export lambs.

Intensive mixed livestock farming, with dairying and lamb-fattening pre-dominant, and the variety of terrain and of physical setting found in Piako-Matamata, swell in more extensive form over the low hills that separate the Waihou-Piako valley from the Waikato valley above Ngaruawahia; interrupted only by swamps still to be reclaimed, it extends in intensive form into the bottom-lands of the Waipa and beyond Te Awamutu into the Otorohanga basin where, on all sides, much hillier sheep-farming landscapes shut it in. A line joining Piopio, Te Kuiti and Putaruru marks approximately its southern limit, beyond which the valley land and easy interfluves rise quickly to 500 and then to 1,000 feet. Here tributaries of the main rivers have deeply dissected the northern rim of the Volcanic Plateau's ignimbrite surface, or have more rudely cut a jumble of razor-back ridges and narrow valleys into the King Country's weak Eocene and Oligocene sediments. This is a country of sheep, of hill pastures, of forest plantations and still-standing bush, and it is much more sparsely settled.

It is seventy miles – difficult miles on a tortuous road through steep hill country on which even sheep are thinly spread and over bush-clad Mount Messenger – from Te Kuiti to Urenui where the coastal dairylands of Taranaki commence and reach along the littoral around, and inland of, the cloud-hidden cone of Egmont to beyond Patea. On the other hand, it is only thirty miles over the Kaimais from Matamata to Tauranga: and the landscape of intensive mixed livestock farming starts again ten miles short of Tauranga. Dairying and fat lamb raising – with here and there a cluster of farms on which increasing interest is being shown in the breeding and fattening of beef cattle, and loose strings of smaller holdings which provide mounting evidence of the profitability of citrus fruit, tamarillos, Chinese gooseberries and other exotic subtropical fruit – reach around the crescent coast of the Bay of Plenty from Waihi to Te Kaha. The lowland is at first hemmed in sharply by the Kaimais, gives way gradually to narrow, warm and sheltered valleys separated by flat-topped ridges south of Te Puke, is pinched out west of Matata, where the vol-canic rocks of the interior push out to the coast, and again at Whakatane Heads, where narrow greywacke projections of the axial ranges thrust northwards into the sea. Beyond Opotiki the plain is narrow and cramped and hemmed in by the dissected Cretaceous flanks of the Raukumara range. But everywhere that terrain allows, and especially on the partially drained Rangitaiki plain, there is a dense livestock population with the grade Jersey cow and her butterfat the focus of farmers' attention, the basis of their daily round of routine tasks and the explanation of their social life and attitudes; and the foundation hitherto of the region's prosperity.

Sheep farming landscapes

In New Zealand the sheep is the principal denizen of the hills and mountain-sides; and of hills, hill country and high country slopes, there is in New

Zealand a plenitude. The sheep, the sheepmen, the sheepruns, and the grey and craggy high country landscape of the South Island have been described elsewhere. Most sheep, however, are in the wet, rough-hewn, formerly thickly forested hill country of the North Island. Almost half the island is steep and corrugated hill country; another quarter is hilly but has easier slopes and is not so thoroughly broken and dissected. *Grand Hills for Sheep** is the title of a novel describing life in such country. Fine, ideal, appropriate to the husbandry of sheep, the green hills of the North Island may well be in this age of the hormone sprays, penicillin, topdressing aircraft and articulated stockliners. But a century ago the same hills were blanketed with a dense, tangled, dripping forest, dark, almost impenetrable, rarely pierced even by tree-shaded corridors along muddy tracks worn by the Maori.

A third of all the sheep in New Zealand, at least 20 million, graze the pastures on the hills and in the narrow papa gorges and defiles that dissect them and the occasional strings of valley flats in two major regions of almost uninterrupted hill country. One extends from the mouth of the Waikato southwards, west of the Volcanic Plateau and inland of the coastal dairy belt of Taranaki and the Manawatu plain until, across the Pohangina river, it ends abruptly against the fault face of the Ruahine and Mokai Patea ranges. The other runs from Cape Palliser to East Cape between the sea and the main ranges. Within this northeast–southwest elongation of jumbled hills only two pockets of coastal plain – the Hawke's Bay and the Poverty Bay flats – and the structurally longitudinal trough of the Wairarapa graben break the continuity and configurational monotony of steep hills, narrow valleys, deep dissection and abrupt, often precipitous, slopes.

So thorough was the fluvial dissection of these terrains, so narrow and razor-backed the summit ridges, so deep the narrow gorges in the weak Tertiary and Cretaceous mudstone, sandstone and siltstone, and so steep the pervading slopes, that even the impenetrable tangle of storied forest was unable, under the periodic torrential rains that occurred, to maintain the stability of soil, regolith and weathered sedimentary rocks. Mass movement, induced by torrential rains and aided and encouraged by shattering earthquakes, scarred the forested slopes, choked valleys and dammed lakes, and had created a morphology of landforms that, when revealed by deforestation, was seen to be weird and fantastic as if indeed the mythical Maori ancestor, Maui, may in fact and not merely in legend have fished it from beneath the surface of the Pacific a few hundred years ago. When the vegetative cover was removed and the root anchors of former forest giants rapidly decayed, mass movement was incited to speed and extend its work of slope destruction. The volume and power of running water were reinforced in their task of removing the weak materials deposited in the

* Georgina McDonald, *Grand Hills for Sheep*, 2nd edn., Christchurch, Whitcombe and Tombs, 1949.

courses of rivers and at the foot of slopes in steeply graded catchments, and of transporting them from land to sea.

But the removal of the bush is part – perhaps the most important part – of New Zealand history: it is an epic of ruthless, efficient yet thoughtless conversion of an almost virgin natural landscape to a countryside whose appearance is of man's making, a saga of European pioneering in a frighteningly alien environment. Axe and fire-stick were the symbols of progress in the prodigal decades of subjugating the forest. The story is nowhere better told than in Guthrie Smith's classic *Tutira*.

It took some decades before the first European occupiers of North Island hill land discovered techniques for transforming the vegetation and the face of the land by converting fern, or scrub, or bush, to pasture. Sometimes a generation of toil and heartbreak went in vain; and the aggressive indigenous vegetation of the heavy rainfall districts reoccupied its rightful domain.

The bush – cool and shady, damp and dripping – was difficult to burn even in a dry summer. The 'bush burn' technique evolved was to underscrub the lower forest storey and fell the trees of smaller girth in winter and spring and, taking advantage of a suitable dry spell in autumn – in February or March – and a favourable wind, to set it alight. A good fire would then be liable to run for miles and to consume the vegetation of ages converting the ground cover and felled understorey to ash and reducing the ancient forest giants to blackened stumps. The tang and trace of forest fires was apparent over most of the North Island and indeed often up to 100 miles out to sea to leeward of the land. The summer sun glowed brick red in the universal haze for weeks on end. Such fires created a black and ghostly landscape. The ground was covered with ash and littered with logs that smouldered for weeks and were rekindled into flame periodically by shifting winds, even into the following winter.

Meanwhile a seed mixture was sown by hand on to the warm ashes. Before the winter the grey and blackened hillsides assumed a suspicion of a thin green vegetative cover. Sheep were turned on to the new grass, not so much to graze it as to trample soil and ash and induce tillering of grass and clovers. The fertility of the ash assured good pasture growth even from the inferior seed mixtures so often employed. At least the inferior grasses and clovers throve for a year or two.

But soon the indigenous vegetative vigour re-exerted itself. Manuka seed sprouted and grew a myriad seedlings; bracken fern fronds uncoiled and bidi-bidi took root, and in damper situations, hard fern and the alien blackberry and the other pioneers of secondary forest growth – rewarewa, five finger and whitey wood – appeared. The scrub had to be cut by teams of Maoris or Indians, or fired standing. This time there was little or no ash, and the flames did not traverse all the hillside. Many steeper slopes had to be abandoned. On the best of them, even with hand sowing of phosphate by Maori gangs, it was a never-ending struggle until aerial topdressing of artificial fertilizers and the aerial spraying of hormone weed killers after World War II eased the struggle. In many cases, and over millions of acres of tougher terrain, these alone have assured man's fight to subdue the hill country vegetation and soils of the North Island a deferred but successful outcome.

In fern and scrub country it was the livestock that chewed and trod and thrashed the indigenous plants into subjugation. Bracken fern would carry a hot fire which left a temporary thin cover of fertility in which sown grass and clover took root. But it left also the fern's rhizomes deep in the soil, and with the gentle touch of heat from the following spring's sunshine, the curled gingery-chocolate fronds appeared and in weeks would have smothered almost any introduced plants, except possibly only gorse and blackberry, in a man-high tangle of impenetrable bracken had it not been for the pioneers' livestock. These he used by forcing them, if he had brought in sufficient stock and erected adequate fencing, to chew off every soft curled frond of fern. Wethers were best at the job. But most hill country had thin leached topsoils on deeply weathered clay subsoils, excessively dry in summer and cold and wet in winter. They did not have the inherent fertility to support good pasture. Though the fern may well be subdued, other weeds – native and alien – invaded the often thin and open pasture of low fertility grasses. Burning only destroyed the shallow humus layer and bared the ground without destroying the capsuled seed of manuka and gorse. Many hill country areas were abandoned during the 1930s within a generation or two of their first settlement. Others, even some of the best of them, had a steady or declining livestock population until revolutionary and very much more successful techniques of topdressing, weed spraying and grazing management were introduced in the last twenty-five years.

Farm development of hill country required more time, greater acreages, larger numbers of stock and, above all, large-scale capital. The dairy lands were occupied and developed by men with little capital, worked in family units with wife and children helping in the monotonous routine task of milking, and with cooperative enterprise handling processing and marketing. The hill country sheep stations were developed by hired labour or contract gangs. Holdings range from several hundred up to thousands of acres and are operated either by the owner or his manager employing stockmen and shepherds and contract shearing, fencing and scrubcutting gangs and topdressing firms to sow precious trails of fertility from the air.

The traditional pattern of hill country sheep farming is perhaps best seen in the lower ranges east of the Wairarapa, in the tangle of slip-scarred hills inland of Hawke's Bay, or in deep valleys of the East Coast north of the Poverty Bay flats where in many cases the bentonitic shales and deeply weathered mudstones are virtually crumbling, collapsing and filling once narrow valleys, with clear streams, to a depth of hundreds of feet with grey detritus after a short sixty years of pastoral occupancy. These are store-stock rearing reservoirs.

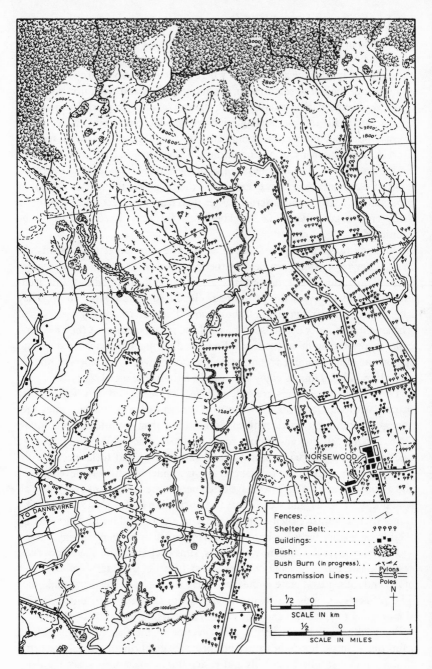

17. *Wairarapa hill country sheep farm landscape*

The pattern of hill country livestock rearing is most firmly and substantially established in the hills east of Masterton, Eketahuna, Pahiatua and Dannevirke. Here the terrain is less elevated and slopes less steep than in the valleys cut into the eastern flanks of the axial ranges where livestock numbers are often falling as a result of the toll of soil erosion, declining fertility and weed invasion. East of the Wairarapa, catchments are small, streams less steeply graded and rainfall less phenomenally intense. Precipitation averages less than 60 inches. Ten-year twenty-four-hour intensities amount to only 4 or 5 inches, less than half the short duration intensity of precipitation to be expected in the Hawke's Bay or East Coast valleys. The bush was not as dense and continuous. The establishment of danthonia swards was easier and the reversion tendencies are not as pronounced. Light manuka scrub, rather than hard fern, secondary forest and damp-encouraged aliens like blackberry, is the only weed invader to be countered.

Holdings range from 500 to 5,000 acres. They are larger out towards the coast. They have often been held by the same family for three or four generations. The timber-built homesteads are large and commodious and well-established, usually now almost 100 years old. The owners are well-to-do. They have time to take part in tasks off the station. They are frequently members of parliament, of county councils, of the wool and meat boards or of their electoral colleges, prominent office holders in Federated Farmers, directors of stock and station and other prominent companies, racehorse owners, members of hunt or polo clubs. Their families enjoy status and a fashionable social round.

Their broad green acres are hilly but clear of weeds and only superficially scarred with slips and other evidence of accelerated soil erosion. They are, however, often underused; with modern, rather than traditional techniques, their carrying capacity and output could be doubled or trebled. But with high rates of tax and adequate incomes, landholders have had little incentive for many years to invest more capital and labour, undertake further development and assume greater risks. They have often been more inclined to develop small stud flocks, or herds, and seek repute and distinction in the livestock show ring rather than to improve their carrying capacity, output and returns by selecting their livestock not for looks but for its performance by progeny testing.

The representative station, 1,740 acres, runs back from the Tauwheru river east of Masterton. The front country is easy hills and includes some 200 acres of flat and rolling land close to the river. Here are the homestead and buildings. The property extends narrowly two miles into the hills with much steeper slopes rising to 1,600 feet and views out to the coast north of Castle Point.

Practically all is in pasture. A small section of the flat, littered still with kahikatea stumps, floods in winter but provides good rough grazing for cattle in dry summers. The front hills and easier slopes – 500 acres – are regularly topdressed. They have good pastures with ryegrass and clovers. A low broad

King country: North Island sheep country
Lush topdressed pasture growth on deforested hills and a flock of Romney ewes mustered
in the cool of morning before the valley fog has lifted.

ridge close to the homestead has been smoothed by bulldozing to provide one of the many farm airstrips in the district. At the top of the ridge, to which a metalled road provides access for trucks, are the concrete-block bulk fertilizer bins. But most of the farm – the steeper valleys and narrow ridges more than three-quarters of a mile from the homestead – have never been topdressed. The pastures here are dominated by danthonia – an induced indigenous species – with browntop and Yorkshire fog and *Lotus* spp. on damper cooler southern faces. These pastures tend to run to manuka. Every few years large open patches of the white flowering shrub are cut with the slasher and lie russet on the ground until autumn, when they are burned. The larger burned-over patches may on occasions be hand sown with grass and clover seed.

The breeding flock consists of 2,700 mixed-age coarse-woolled Romney ewes. Both Romney and Southdown rams are used, the former on the younger ewes to breed replacements for the flock, the latter on the five and six year old ewes to produce fat lambs. Lambing percentage is about 90, slightly below the national average. The 900 female Romney, or 'white-faced' lambs, are retained on the farm. The male or wether Romney lambs are sold. The quicker maturing crossbred lambs, fattened on front country pastures before most of them are closed-up for hay are drafted expertly on sight and by touch in a crush pen in late December as soon as 'killable' and sent to the freezing works at Wellington for slaughter. The Romney wether lambs are weaned at the same time and may be sold later as stores, or sent fat to the works, depending on the season and their condition. The cast-for-age ewes are also disposed of in January or February. The previous year's ewe lambs – now 'two-tooths' – are drafted in January. Most of them, 600 or so, are selected for retention in the flock. The remainder, a line of 250–300, are sold at the Dannevirke two-tooth autumn fair in February.

There are also 132 breeding cows on the station, thirty-three of them together with three sires (one imported) comprising a horned Hereford stud. The stud cattle are kept mainly in the small grassy paddocks close to the homestead and woolshed. Only as yearlings do they climb the hills. The other breeding cows are kept mainly to graze the sheep pastures, to eat out rougher growth and to penetrate the swampy floors of the narrow valleys where sheep rarely venture.

The winter stocking of the station's 1,740 acres is less than three 'ewe equivalents' per acre, probably less than half its potential capacity.

Winter is bleak especially on the hill pastures exposed to the west and south, and the gravel flats in front of the homestead can be frosty. Although in the past the drier flats have been used to grow winter fodder – turnips, rape and lucerne – the only auxiliary feed now is hay taken from smaller enclosures on the flats and ploughable hill slopes in December or January. Some 3,000 bales are harvested with the station's own range of expensive equipment. It is fed out to the stud and other cattle in winter, or in autumn, should a dry spell intervene. For this purpose, as well as to aid mustering, fencing and fence renewal, bulldozed tracks have been cut up both sides of the main valley which divides the property; they give tractor access to all but the three largest and most remote enclosures.

The homestead, with its tennis court, is dignified with spacious lawns, weeping elms and exotic conifers and shrubs, and nestles on the flat at the entrance to this valley. Across the stream, which is lined with willows and tall poplars, is the manager's house and a large hut with bunks where the shepherd and any casual labour (including the itinerant shearing gang) are accommodated. Close by are both sheep and cattle yards – hot and dusty in summer despite the shade of leafy poplars, but chill and muddy in winter – and the massive five-stand shearing shed. Behind the shed and out on to the flat which reaches to the main access road and station entrance near the Tauwheru river are the smaller hay paddocks grazed usually by the red and white stud Hereford cattle, by ewes and fattening lambs, and by the station hacks, seven of them. Behind the wool-shed, in kennels raised off the ground, is a barking pack of no fewer than twelve sheep dogs – a mongrel assortment of colours, black eye dogs, blue heeling dogs, brown and shaggy huntaways and collie heading dogs.

From 1960 to 1965 the income on such a station from wool alone averaged a little under $14,000. In 1967 this was cut by almost half.

Both within and beyond the major blocks of North Island hill country – in the South Island, too, especially in Southland where indoor winter feeding of

19. *Southland: South Island downland near Mataura*
Formerly cultivated and cropped, this downland now carries a dense sheep population on permanent pastures heavily limed and topdressed.

the ewe flock is being pioneered – are less traditional patterns of hill sheep farming and sheep farming countryside.

A farm twenty-two miles from Auckland's Queen Street, seven miles east of the motorway, may be taken to portray more recent developments and less traditional management and procedures. The unit comprises two properties, one of 270 acres and one of 400 acres, separated by one small 23-acre holding and a quarter of a mile of road. The road runs two miles along the boundary of the smaller property and stops at the entrance to the larger, beyond which a newly cut bulldozed track climbs steeply up the faulted greywacke face of the larger property to an elevation of over 700 feet and to broad interfluves. Half of this property is in dense second growth forest. A few years ago the smaller property carried 200–300 sheep. It had once been used in part as a dairy farm but was too steep to be economic. When taken over four years ago by the present owner and his son – both professional men working in Auckland – half the smaller, lower farm had reverted to mature 10 to 15 feet high 'old man' gorse. The larger section of land was unfarmed (its former owner met overhead expenses by quarrying greywacke road metal) and over half of its 200 acres not in bush was occupied by manuka, bracken fern, blackberry and gorse. On both properties deep narrow valleys sheltered relict patches of stock-damaged bush – with mature puriri, taraire, rimu and kahikatea.

Much of the gorse has been crushed by bulldozer and tractor and burned. On slopes too steep for mechanical aids, gorse has been sprayed with 2-45D hormone weedkiller or, like the manuka, burned standing. New subdivision fences have been erected to provide to date twenty-seven paddocks. In place of the normal seven-wire fence with heavy concrete or timber strainer posts and battens every 2 feet, fencing with ten high-tensile wires and with light, chemically treated timber posts but without battens, or fences with seven wires, three of them electrified from the main power supply, have been used. Heavy initial capital topdressings with molybdic superphosphate have been used to stimulate white clover growth; and annual maintenance topdressings of 3 hundredweights per acre to establish balanced ryegrass–white clover swards.

But the credit for the establishment of good pastures goes to the livestock employed. Already on the 400 acres at present in grass almost eight ewe equivalents per acre are carried. Mob stocking with ewes has prevented the return of gorse, bracken, blackberry and manuka. Mob stocking (as opposed to 'set stocking') involves the rotation every two or three days of the entire flock from pasture to pasture giving a short-term stock density of 150 to 200 ewes per acre so that every vestige of green, even unpalatable growth, is chewed down to the roots and the ground heavily dunged. Beef-breeding cows have been used to crush the dead but standing fire-blackened wood of gorse and manuka, and to eat out and trample blackberry and bracken. With the late spring flush of pasture growth, stimulated by heavy dunging and artificial fertilizers, the few pastures in which slopes are such as to allow tractor-drawn machines, hay balers and heavy trucks to operate are closed to grazing. Hay is also purchased from outside. This is fed out in winter to the breeding cows by throwing it amongst the standing gorse and manuka after autumn firing not only to encourage the cattle to crush the standing sticks but also to seed the ground with grass and clover.

On this farm a Perendale flock is grazed. It might better be said, is 'used'. The Perendale is a breed evolved in New Zealand in the last twenty-five years by crossing Romney and Cheviot. It is hardier than the Romney, capable of surviving on pickings, or on gorse and manuka seedlings, agile on the hills, with a lighter but finer fleece (50/52s) and a higher twinning rate and, most important in this particular case where regular shepherding is out of the question, requires little attention at lambing time. Today the flock consists of 1,400 mixed-age ewes together with 700 hoggets. Only Perendale rams are used. Wether lambs are sold fat mainly off their mothers in December or January, usually to the 'works'. Others are sold to the local butchers' markets in small batches through the autumn and winter. The city fat stock saleyards are only eight miles away. Hoggets are mated at seven months of age and from each year's hoggets 200 are selected on the basis of weight gain, early maturity, wool weight and quality, and their dams' history of twinning to form a recorded (not a stud) flock. Each is tagged as a new-born lamb so that its performance can subsequently be documented. In a similar way some fifty or sixty ram lambs are retained and their weight gain and wool growth recorded. In this way, a flock is being established, not on the basis of conformation or prima donna show ring appearance, but on tried and tested performance and productivity. Lambing percentage has already been lifted from 85 (already good for unshepherded ewes 'done so hard') to over 110.

Now that the bulk of the crushing has been done by Aberdeen Angus breeding cows – ninety were employed – these are being replaced by Friesian bulls bought as weaners from town milk supply dairy farms south of Auckland and reared until they have, at eighteen months of age, a carcass weight of 600 pounds and so provide ideal lean meat for the fast expanding and highly remunerative export market for manufacturing beef. Bulls have been shown to make greater weight gains than steers or heifers; and Friesian bulls have been proved to do this faster than the traditional beef breeds which in any case produce much more fat and less lean.

This, then, is a hill country farm of a future, rather than traditional, New Zealand pattern, producing a finer wool than the average Romney flocks and much more lean 'dairy beef' per acre than the beef breeds are capable of doing. It is an untidy looking farm, with green pastures grazed at all seasons (except when closed briefly for hay) to within an inch of the soil surface, broken by steep faces of tawny hormone-sprayed gorse, black stems of manuka, patches of residual indigenous forest, scattered old macrocarpa trees and fenced-off, slip-

20. *East Coast: North Island sheep country*
Typical layout of sheep yards designed for one-man three-way drafting of stock. View from woolshed.

eroded slopes where hybrid poplars and radiata pines have been planted, yet carrying a density of livestock higher than that on many, if not most, farms on New Zealand's best and easiest lowland pastures. It is favoured by closeness to markets, freezing works and fertilizer works, and to contractors and suppliers. It is favoured, too, by its northerly frost-free locality and all-year-round greenness. It is operated by weekend farmers ('Queen Street farmers') with most of the development operations – aerial topdressing, fencing, shearing, weed spraying, hay making – being undertaken by contractors, so that the only mechanical capital investment outside the shearing shed is a secondhand tractor, a portable chain saw and motorized knapsack sprayer. Livestock management is done very largely at the weekend and, in summer, in the early morning and evening by the owner's son. A generation ago such a farm would have required three or four men employed full-time, half a dozen hacks and a team of several dogs. Today one horse, one dog, a secondhand tractor and a mini car suffice. Mustering is often done now by taking the mini on clay tracks, the dog riding in the open boot to the scene of his tasks, and a luggage rack serving to carry sick or stubborn sheep or posts and battens for mending a battered fence on the way. The only labour regularly employed is on a part-time basis, mainly for feeding-out hay in winter. Yet the farm carries on its 400 presently grazeable acres of pasture no fewer than 3,150 livestock units or ewe equivalents. With further development of another hundred acres, and employing similar labour-saving techniques, the unit could push its capacity up to almost 4,500 ewe equivalents, or nine per acre.

Most North Island hill country is rugged and untidy. The strange wilderness of deep dissection arises in part from its structural recency, continued tectonic disturbance, the weakness of the deep-bedded Cretaceous and Tertiary sandstones and mudstones, and the phenomenally intense rains. High temperatures and humidity have weathered the soft rocks to great depth. Forest formerly carpeted, smoothed and held in place this deep regolith of clay. The substitution of grass for trees – early a thin and discontinuous sward of grass – has induced erosion in weird and unusual forms. Gullies, slips and slides, mudflows and crumbling valley sides moving with every rainstorm, liable on occasions to bring from 10 to 30 inches of precipitation in three or four days, have maimed and scarred the landscape with raw and ugly slips. Bush remnants, tortured slopes invaded by weeds, valley floors where formerly clear water trickled in a rocky bed now choked to a depth of hundreds of feet with grey detritus over which the flooding river picks tortuous and braided paths – these are but part of the witness to the unintended outcome of human interference and to the potency of man not only in transforming the vegetation and the outward appearance of the landscape but also as a geomorphological and hydrological agent. Wide areas of less accessible hill country still have their cover of dull khaki green bush, only its understorey and groundcover transformed by deer and goats and wild cattle. But the bulk of the once forested hills have, especially since the advent of aerial topdressing, been successfully converted to pastoral use. Grass green hills, ridge and valley on ridge and valley, reaching for miles, form an expansive corrugated sheep walk extensively farmed. Here man has not changed significantly the strange, contorted, fantastically deformed and dissected geomorphic outline of the hill country terrain. But elsewhere accelerated erosion is rife. In some areas it occurs on a scale beside which man's puny efforts to restrict it by planting trees are pointless. Yet, even where man-induced erosion of soil and land surface is at its worst, man has as yet only partially, if frighteningly and appallingly, speeded up age-long natural processes of earth sculpturing.

Mixed-crop livestock farming landscapes

New Zealand has little flat or near-flat land. In the South Island the plains are built of coarse greywacke gravels from the wasting alpine highland. Three thousand feet of uniformly coarse rounded gravels and shingle underlie the largest lowland of easy slope in the whole country – the Canterbury plains. In the North Island the alluvial lowlands are more often built of finer materials derived from reassorted pumice and the fine-grained waste from weak Tertiary rocks. In the north and everywhere west of the ranges, from the Ruawai flats in Northland to the Manawatu plain, the lowlands are green with finely divided pastures and thick with grazing livestock. Indeed it is cows, mainly Jersey cows, all the way from Otaki to Kaitaia.

Only east of the ranges – especially on the Hawkes Bay and Poverty Bay alluvial flats – are lighter rainfall, lower humidities, occasional dry nor'west winds and high sunshine hours comparable with and reminiscent of those of the Canterbury, Wairau and Tasman Bay plains of the South Island. With the exception of inland irrigated basins in Central Otago and outer suburban market gardens adjacent to most centres of population agglomeration, these sheltered and drier lowland areas on, or close to, the eastern littoral of both islands comprise the exceptional in the prevailing gross pattern of New Zealand pastoral agriculture and the prevalence of uniformly green pastures in the rural landscape. Here alone is tillage a regular feature of the agricultural economy and of the rural scene. Here alone are the rich, warm, varied and changing colours of soil recently turned and of crops harvest ripe persistent and characteristic elements in the countryside. But this richer diversity of landscape and economy, this mixing of cropping and livestock rearing, is confined to the plains, extending only occasionally up the adjacent slopes where these are gentle and rounded and smoothly contoured enough to be termed 'downland' rather than 'hill country'. But all the way from Tuatapere, at the gateway to Fiordland, to Tikitiki, in the shadow of East Cape – from the oats and bitter southerly squalls and Scottish farmers of Southland to the maize and kumara patches, intense tropical rains and Maori villages of the East Coast – the limited lowland areas of mixed cultivation are shut in, or pinched out, by hill and mountain country in which the sheep is king. Indeed grass and sheep are important, too, on many cropland farms.

When the European first saw them the Canterbury plains were an expanse of tussock grasses glittering in the sun and buffeted by the parched nor'wester that roared out of the inland mountain gorges. The stretch of tussock was broken only by the sometimes mile-wide grey-white beds of river shingle let down abruptly in deep trenches into the plains and threaded with the pale blue strings of braided streams. The thorny wild irishman (*Discaria toumatou*), the rigid, green, leathery spikes of the spaniard (*Aciphylla colensoi*) and tall open clumps of cabbage trees (*Cordyline australis*) alone relieved the monotonous tawny expanse of waving tussock grasses.

First, the grassy plains were parcelled out into sheep runs, each embracing tens of thousands of acres and reaching from riverbed to riverbed, unfenced, its boundaries guarded at strategic points by chained dogs trained to bark at the

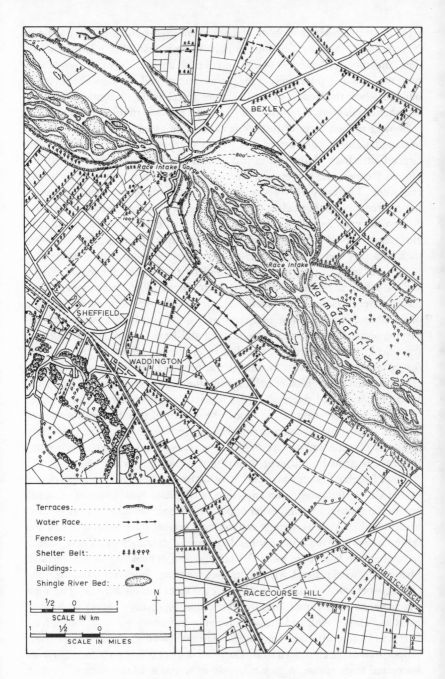

21. *Canterbury mixed crop-livestock farm landscape*

sight of straying Merinos. With the advent of gold-mining in Australia and New Zealand, the mounting food imports of an industrializing United Kingdom, the importation into New Zealand of capital and the construction of railway, the loess and gravel soils of the plains were turned, the tussocks ploughed out and, where the loess was thin, the larger gravel boulders laboriously heaped together in piles which remain today as rocky mounds in many paddocks.

Some 4 million acres of tussock land was cultivated and the South Island lowland landscape transformed. For twenty years wheat was the bonanza. The larger Canterbury plains estates had each upwards of 5,000 acres under the plough. Reapers and binders operated in echelon, twenty or more to each large enclosure. The temporary encampments, where ploughmen and harvesters lived, often formed the nucleus of later 'village' settlements and service centres. At first the gravelly yellow-grey soils yielded rich harvests of wheat and oats. But uninterrupted cropping quickly exhausted their virgin fertility, destroyed their structure and, before the shelterbelts that were being planted had chance to mature, led to the stripping of topsoil by the violent nor'wester. Wheat yielded at first 20 bushels or more to the acre. In the 1880s this fell by a quarter. Later, water races were dug to lead water from the rivers of the foothill margin of the plains, at an elevation of 1,100 to 1,300 feet, across the piedmont's unvarying slope alongside the gorse-planted sod-bank boundaries of paddocks from field to field towards the sea. The races provided water for livestock and for farmhouse use and so facilitated the breaking up of larger estates, the closer internal subdivision of holdings and the more intensive use of land away from the entrenched riverbeds where previously surface water was lacking.

It was the depression of the 1890s, the advent of new political forces and ideas, and institutional and technological changes that brought the next transformation of scene, and which established patterns of land use and farm economy that have remained fundamentally unaltered since the century began.

Large leasehold estates were cut up: other freehold estates were repurchased by the Crown for subdivision and closer settlement. New forms of leasehold tenure were introduced and easier opportunities for purchase by small farmers made possible. Arable cropping and livestock rearing were wedded in new and more intensive mixed economies and systems of management. These were at the same time less risky, more flexible and less demanding on soil fertility. Shelterbelts were planted, wire fences used for closer subdivision and the water race network intensified. Farms of 200 to 500 acres became the rule. The horse was replaced by machines; oats by other crops, especially pastures for hay and grass and clover seed, and brassicas for supplementary winter livestock feed. Fertilizers came into use. Improved rotational pastures occupied increasing proportions of the cultivated land. The relative place of livestock and cash crops fluctuated from season to season largely in response to the price of wool on Christchurch auction floors and of 'Canterbury' lamb at Smithfield market.

22. *Canterbury plains: mixed crop-livestock farming*
The inner margin of the plains where the Waimakariri debouches from its highland gorge and has cut suites of terraces into the gravels of the piedmont. The nor'west wind whips fine sediments from the riverbed and sprays them on the southbank farmlands, protected by shelterbelts and gorse sodbank hedges. Intensive cultivation of cereal and fodder crops and livestock fattening.

The regularity of the visual pattern of the Canterbury plains landscape belies the detailed variety of farm practice. The plains provide the largest extent of regular rectangular checkerboard subdivision in the country. Roads and properties and field boundaries run straight and at right-angles. Farm boundaries are often marked by thick, tall, dark windbreaks of radiata pines. Sodbank fences remain, their gorse hedges trimmed and pruned today by machines. Pastures, crops and newly turned soil alternate. Grass, however, is the main crop, even on farms with most cash crops. Roads, a chain wide, with greywacke shingle carriageways and wide broom or gorse-filled verges, sometimes run straight for from ten to twenty miles, with the snowtipped summits of the mountains of the inland ranges visible ahead framed by parallel shelterbelts of pines and gums. The slope up towards the inner margin of the plains, where fields are larger and where with a heavier rainfall pastures run to browntop, is imperceptible to the eye. But driving into the face of a howling, hot nor'wester even a modern car is alive to the extra energy demanded by dusty wind and persistent grade.

The only non-rectangular element in the cultural landscape are the broad sinuous curves of the irrigation channel across the upper part of the mid-Canterbury plain. It follows approximately the gently curved contours from the apex of the fan of the Rangitata river to the barely discernible convexity of the overlapping shingle cone of the Rakaia river carrying a thousand cusecs of the Rangitata's flow. In winter the water, not now used to keep pastures green or to promote the growth of lucerne and clover hay, is plunged over the angular suite of terraces down to the Rakaia riverbed, and its 300-foot fall used to generate 25,000 kW of electricity at the Highbank station.

Few portions of the rural scene in New Zealand change with the passing of the seasons as do the ploughed and cultivated landscapes of Canterbury. In winter when southwesterly squalls sometimes deposit a thin cover of snow over the face of the foothills and higher parts of the plains, the landscape is drab and lacks colour. The wet soils are dark and match the black and serried outline of shelterbelts. Pasture growth ceases and rich greens are preserved only where a farmer has conserved autumn growth for his lambing ewes. Other sheep graze on breakfed turnips; still others, enclosed in high densities on almost bare stubble paddocks white with hoar frost, are fed hay.

In spring green is the pervading colour as the rotational pastures make rapid growth. Tractors purr and are followed by attendant flocks of seagulls as they prepare the ground for seed; and new-sown pastures, clover, lucerne and grain crops gradually hide the fast-warming light soil with at first a tinge of pale green and then a lush growth of the deep green one associates with nitrogen-rich soils until the different crops acquire the varied hues and greater height of approaching maturity. The trimmed gorse hedges, more apparent now than in the duller landscape of winter, sparkle with gold and on almost every farm lambing time is a main focus of attention.

Summer is heralded by the growing strength, frequency and warmth of the nor'wester in November and December. Away from the coast it blows with monotonous and oppressive regularity, howling in the shelterbelts, carrying dust from the exposed riverbeds across the plains, tiring man and beast. Quite abruptly the greens disappear as pastures dry out and seed heads form. The grain turns first yellow and then harvest gold. Hay is mown and baled. The combine harvester devours its crop of ryegrass, cocksfoot or white clover and deposits valuable sacks of certified seed at intervals in the paddocks. Lambs are fattened on the aftermath, or on rape grown for the purpose, and go off to the freezing works in January. Then the cash crops – 55 bushels to the acre of Arawa, Aotea and Tainui wheat, barley for brewing, peas, blue lupins – are harvested. In dry late summers lucerne, chou mollier, rape and turnips may be grazed by late lambs, ewes ready for the works and beef cattle. The potato crop is lifted and heaped in long straw- and earth-covered tumuli until shipped in winter to North Island urban markets.

In autumn there is more green in the pastures and paddocks of winter fodder crops. The soil is ploughed and crop stubble burned-off or turned under. The richer colours of harvest time have gone. The year's livestock production is now off the farm and new flocks of cast-for-age ewes are being assembled at autumn sales. They come from the high country, foothills and downland.

No two farms are alike and few are similar in their economy and management – though terrain and soils are often uniform over wide areas. Farms range all the way from those with half their acreage annually in cash grain and seed crops, with few livestock, to those on which the plough is used only to renew pastures and lucerne and where livestock, including recently more Aberdeen Angus and Hereford cattle, are the only source of income. This is especially the case on the coastal fringe of the plains for here, although rainfall is lower, soils are heavier and the water table high. Close to Christchurch pastures on former swampland are permanent. Here Friesian cows are milked for town supply. Livestock, pastures and green fodder crops, rather than cash crops, are prominent, too, where irrigation water is available, even though soils may be light and gravelly and their loess cover thin. The most gravelly portions of the plains, usually close to the north bank of the major rivers, have larger holdings, on which occasional patches of tussock, matagowrie and manuka scrub remain. Sometimes the plough has never been used and stands of exotic timber trees have been planted. Here country towns and the crossroad service centres are absent.

Orchard and market garden landscapes

The landscapes of intensive cultivation are few, small and pocketed. For New Zealand they are unusual and distinctive. Specialized crop production seeks out special advantages of soil and climate or of location with respect to the larger urban markets. It is not surprising that the two largest areas, the Heretaunga plains, around Hastings in Hawke's Bay, and the Tasman Bay lowland, between Nelson and Motueka, and one of the fastest growing – the Bay of Plenty waste-land south of Tauranga and sheltered valleys inland of it – are the sunniest localities in the country. All these are cosily sheltered from prevailing blustery west and southwest winds. Indeed Napier, Nelson and Tauranga are rivals almost every year in the competition for the city enjoying most hours of bright sunshine. It usually exceeds 2,400, or even 2,500 hours.

Nor is it surprising that, in order of acreage of intensive cultivation, the Auckland outer suburban region stands next after Hawke's Bay and Tasman Bay. Indeed it is the clear leader in the extent and number of its market gardens.

23. Pukekohe Hill, South Auckland
The gentle slopes of the scoria cone, 25 miles from Auckland, support intensive market gardening of potatoes, onions, beans, pumpkins, and salad vegetables for the metropolitan market. Casual labour is largely Maori.

The proximity of the country's largest urban market is the key. The scatter of intensive cultivation around the metropolitan agglomeration is remarkably varied – from the growing of pip fruit, grapefruit and vines at Henderson, frequently by Dalmatian orchardists, the asparagus and strawberry patches and glasshouses of tomatoes and table grapes in suburban Mangere, the warm red soils of the Pukekohe volcanic cone famous for their long-keeping onions and early potatoes as well as for their mixed ethnic ownership and operation (Chinese, Indian and European owners and Maori labourers), to the sloping, soil-rilled and newly developed lettuce, cabbage and pumpkin gardens on the Bombay hills. With the outward surging tide of urban expansion, Auckland's orchards and market gardens have been forced to retreat further and further from the auction market; but, withdrawing ahead of the tide of residential and industrial building, they have revealed that soils and climate need not be as vital to success as motorway access to the market, reticulated municipal water supplies and up-to-date methods of cultivation including heavy applications of fertilizer, new seed varieties and especially long, narrow sheets of black polythene for preserving moisture, speeding germination and growth and suppressing weeds.

The isolated cluster of orchards on the Kerikeri Inlet in the Bay of Islands, frost-free, sheltered by pine and poplars and characteristically by broad billowing windbreaks of *Hakea acicularis*, grow citrus and Chinese gooseberries (marketed recently in the United States as 'Kiwi fruit'). Here the 5–10 acre holdings are often the hobby, rather than the business, of immigrants retired early from colonial service in tropical territories in Africa, Asia and the Pacific.

The inland basins of Central Otago are parched and frosty and irrigated. Here, however, nestle the most distinctive orchards in New Zealand, unique in their emphasis on stone fruit. The scatter of apple orchards near Cromwell, the arched string of peach and apricot orchards west of the Clutha river between the hydro station and the town of Roxburgh, are all sharply differentiated from the stark, rocky, depleted and scabweed-ridden schist mountain slopes all around. Pink with blossom, green with subsequent foliage, speckled later with ripe fruit, the orchard enclosures form an abrupt contrast to the dun and arid landscape of adjacent plains and gully-streaked mountain walls. Rainfall is here from 12 to 15 inches, most of it lost by instant runoff and high evaporation after heavy convectional downpours in summer. Yet the climatic extremes of these 'continental' basin floors have some advantages. In the dry atmosphere the incidence of brown rot and black spot is reduced; frosts restrict fungus and virus diseases; high summer temperatures, longer days, and bright sunshine in the clear atmosphere speed the ripening of fruit and enhance its colour. Frosts, though frequent and hard, can be partly avoided on sloping shingle fans above the shallow layer of stagnant air and temperature inversion, and also by employing smudge pots at critical times. As a result Central Otago furnishes 90 per cent of New Zealand's apricots, half its cherries and much of its peaches and plums.

Three areas of intensive cultivation combine orcharding, market gardening, pasture and livestock production, arable cash and fodder crops, contract-growing of crops for factory processing, and special crops like hops, or vines, or tobacco. All are hill or mountain-girt, pocketed flats with fertile, easily worked soils derived from recent alluvium. All are sunny, mild and sheltered; all finely subdivided with richly diversified and colourful landscapes; all are prosperous, their prosperity reflecting the affluent society's expanding demand for luxury foods, for processed crops canned and quick-frozen, for prepared meals, and for exotic and decorative fruit, for vegetables and wines. All are serviced by a city in which large-scale processing plants have been established and have continued to enlarge their activities in recent years, and by ports with both coastal and overseas shipping services. All may soon find that the demand for land for the extension of mixed intensive cultivation and for urban expansion reaches the limits of near-flat land available. In all cases, it is rigidly circumscribed by the steepness of the slopes that confine the pockets of coastal lowland. They are the Tasman Bay lowland, the Heretaunga plain and the Poverty Bay flats.

The Tasman Bay lowland is delimited sharply by fault-angled ranges and most of it occupied by a massive dissected dump of Quaternary (Moutere) gravels, leached, indigenously a billowing sea of manuka frosted with pale blossom, cleared, eroded, and now protected by a vast regiment of dark pines. The alluvial soils are confined to ribbons along the lower part of the Motueka and Waimea valleys and a narrow littoral strip between them. On the seaward toes of the hilly Moutere gravels, pines are replaced patchily by orchards of apples and pears, planted mainly after World War I. But the more unusual forms of intensive land use are on the flat land especially near Motueka and Riwaka. Indeed this area has two crops almost to itself and two unique elements in its rural landscape – tobacco and hops. It produces harvests of flue-cured tobacco leaf and of mechanically harvested hops sufficient to satisfy more than half the nation's demand for cigarettes and pipe tobacco and, surprisingly, all the New Zealanders' enormous thirst for beer which amounts to 23 gallons a head a year, or a quart a day for every male adult.

Tidy little enclosures of green and yellowing tobacco leaf, of tall wired trellises of hops, gardens of raspberries and loganberries and patches of tomatoes are interspersed with pocket handkerchief pastures, occasional poplar-sheltered orchards, and some fields of arable fodder crops, making up a confined but colourful farm landscape of unusual variety. Modern bungalow homes, an assortment of curing sheds, oast houses, packing sheds and implement sheds usually tastefully set amidst domestic gardens, flower beds and banks of blossoming shrubs. Holdings are generally small and rural densities of population high. Sunny little service centres each have their loose cluster of smallholdings. Riwaka, Tasman, Ruby Bay, Dovedale and Sunrise Valley look to Motueka; Appleby, Wakefield, Spring Grove, Hope, Richmond and Stoke look to Nelson, which itself takes part in this intensive cultivation of special crops in its large urban areas under glass culture. But the pockets of intensive cultivation are tiny: and hemming them in are always the dark, scrub- and bush-clad hills which in all directions present steep fault margins to the lowland valleys which they shelter, protect and help to bathe in warm sunshine.

More spectacular and of great topical interest are the Hawke's Bay and Poverty Bay flats. They probably form a significant signpost to the future of New Zealand agriculture and provide a tell-tale indicator of impending changes in parts of the rural landscape. With the establishment and spectacular extension of processing plants at Hastings and Gisborne – aided and stimulated in Gisborne's case by the inauguration of large-scale drainage and flood protection works on the plains – the rural scene has been largely transformed in the last

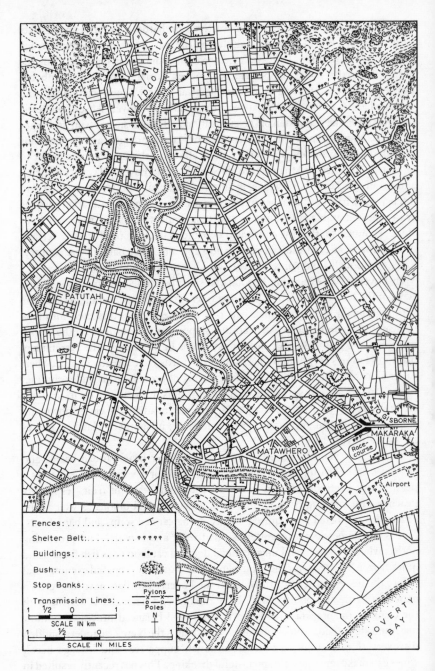

Fences: .... ⊥

Shelter Belt: .... ᵠᵠᵠᵠᵠ

Buildings: .... ▪ ▪ ▪

Bush: .... 🌳

Stop Banks: .... ᴟᴟᴟᴟᴟᴟ

Transmission Lines: ... Pylons / Poles

SCALE IN km

SCALE IN MILES

PATUTAHI

MATAWHERO

MAKARAKA

GISBORNE

Race-course

Airport

POVERTY BAY

Waipaoa River

24. *Poverty Bay intensive crop farm landscape*

decade. Both coastal lowlands had scattered orchards, vineyards and market gardens before World War II; and, during the war, a few smallholders struck gold by growing lilies of the valley, carnations, and other ingredients of the floral tributes that dollar-happy GI's paid to New Zealand's young womanhood. But with the revolution in an affluent postwar society's food technology, and cooking habits, and in kitchen gadgetry (including the universal use of domestic refrigerators), the expansion of the cultivation and processing of fruit and vegetables has been a response to a tremendous demand for canned and frozen foods in both domestic and export markets. The effects of this are nowhere better to be seen in New Zealand than on the Hawke's Bay and Poverty Bay flats. Indeed, almost all the land there which is suitable and available for diversified and intensive use has now been incorporated in orchards, vineyards, market gardens or in repeated arable cultivation of crops on farms which still carry some livestock; so much so, that the continued demand is likely to produce an overflow of such forms of land use and rural landscape into other parts of the country, long, traditionally and conservatively wedded to grass and livestock.

In Poverty Bay expansion beyond the sharply defined limits of the 50,000 acres of the fertile plain of the Waipaoa river is out of the question because the sheep's domain of broken hills, which is at times rudely dissected into fantastically steep and spectacularly eroded slopes, rises abruptly from the inland margin of the plain. But in places smooth hills lie adjacent to the Heretaunga plain in Hawke's Bay, and orchards and vineyards have already climbed their easier slopes: arable cropping and the growing of process crops under contract to the canners are fast spreading over the low hills to the south, on to the light shingly soils of the Ruataniwha plains, and are invading the easier downland slopes of traditional sheep and beef cattle farms in southern Hawke's Bay as far as Waipukurau and Takapau.

The factory demand is basically for peas, runner beans, broad beans, and cobs of sweet corn for quick deep freezing; and for a variety of vegetables – peas, beans, beetroot, carrots, tomatoes, asparagus – and of fruit – especially peaches – for canning. In addition, milk, potatoes, and onions as well as the vegetables just listed are required for preparing canned soups and baby foods. Nor is the domestic pet forgotten, so that meat and fish also find processing outlets whether it be to end up as canned dog and cat food or as fish fingers and quick frozen TV steaks for the suburban family's quickly prepared evening meal before the television screen. In addition the Poverty Bay flats have long grown maize for cattle and poultry food. Now the demand for maize is soaring with the clamour for breakfast foods, corn starch and balanced processed poultry mash and stock foods. But even more spectacular is the New Zealanders' sudden discovery that, in addition to his traditional 'cuppa tea' and 'mugga beer', wines can make for enjoyable and tasteful drinking. This has recently resulted in an explosive planting of the vine.

The pattern of land use and the appearance of the landscape on the Waipaoa plain are changing in several ways. The variegated hues of cropland are replacing pasture greens. Dairy farming is in steep decline. The flats themselves no longer produce sufficient liquid milk to meet even Gisborne's requirements. Abandoned, rusting, tumbled-down, 'walk-through' milking sheds of an older pattern occur on many properties. They are sometimes used today to store lucerne hay, or have been partially converted to serve as packing sheds. Larger mixed livestock farms are being subdivided; and, even on those that retain their earlier extent, increasing acreages are being devoted to the growing of maize year after year without as yet diminution of yields. The corn cobs are either carted off after mechanical harvesting to grain stores and drying plant or poured into corn cribs which have been erected of timber framing and wire netting in many paddocks. These tall, long, narrow structures along a section of the field boundary and filled with golden cobs, are now a characteristic element of the landscape, unique to this part of the country. The grain is sold under contract and at predetermined prices. In consequence of the expansion of the acreage of maize as a cash crop, livestock are now kept in smaller numbers to graze the stubble, pumpkins grown as cattle feed, and the reduced area of pastureland. Dry stock – store lambs and steers from the hill country around – are replacing breeding stock.

On the better soils, especially where they are now protected from flooding, smallholdings are multiplying. Their size may run from five to fifty acres. They often line the main highways across the plains. Between Gisborne and Manutuki – especially at Makaraka and Matawhero – the smallholdings are devoted largely to market gardening and are rarely more than five acres in size. Elsewhere there are peach, apple and citrus orchards sheltered by trimmed poplar windbreaks. Near Waihirere the vine, citrus, fresh flowers, avocado pears, tamarillos and other exotic crops are grown on holdings of from 10 to 20 acres in size. And on most farms on the plains within ten miles of Gisborne livestock fattening and maize growing are increasingly combined with the production of processing crops under contract to local canneries – carrots, beetroot, asparagus, sweet corn, peas, beans, onions, tomatoes, etc. The production of such crops is carefully supervised by the canneries, and the dates of sowing and harvesting so arranged as to provide a steady stream of produce into the processing plant and to make possible the planting of a succession of crops on the same land. Much of the harvesting is done by the processors who, with peas for example, employ giant machines which not only harvest the crop but shell the peas so that they can be delivered to the factory within an hour or so of cutting. Pea hay is subsequently swept up and baled by private contractors. It forms a valuable and increasingly important stock food. Crops that have to be lifted by hand are harvested, bagged and boxed by Maori labour, mainly women. The swelling demand for field workers and for factory operators has in recent years accelerated the movement of Maoris to town. There is a continuing stream of Maoris moving from their traditional lands and villages on the East Coast (north of Poverty Bay) to Gisborne both as seasonal workers and as permanent urban immigrants.

From November on, when the first process crops mature, the Poverty Bay flats become a hive of activity and present a panorama of colour and movement. The teams of gay and gaudily clad, shouting Maori women, the tractors preparing land for later sowing, the giant pea harvesters – and later the red-painted headers and combine harvesters lifting the corn cobs from the tawny fields of ripe maize, the picking of grapes and peaches, the lambs and beef cattle brought in to graze the stubble and vegetable trash, the rich colours of the fertile soils in the summer sun and the variegated shades of manifold crops – all combine to make this a rural landscape of intensive activity, changing colour, high per acre productivity and steeply rising land values.

Beside the subdivision of properties, often enforced by excessively high values and rising levels of local body taxes, and the diminishing average size of holdings, there has now begun a counter movement. So valuable is the land and so intensive are the consequent forms of utilization that the capital necessary is beyond that normally available to an individual New Zealand farmer; and so competitive is the struggle of the processors to ensure a sufficient intake of crops to keep their plant in operation for as long a season as possible, that they themselves are investing increasingly in land and in doing so are amalgamating titles. Not only are the local canneries establishing their own farms and orchards wherever titles to sufficiently large blocks of valuable land can be consolidated, but Auckland vineries, the demand for whose products is expanding faster than they can meet it from the relatively small vineyards in the Auckland outer suburban area, are taking over the small-scale existing vineyards, buying land alongside for planting additional and new varieties of vines and, like the canners and quick-freezers of vegetables and fruit, are contracting with other landowners to plant the vine and to sell the grape crop at prices fixed in advance.

These developments in the vertical integration of farm production and factory processing, involving expert scientific planning and supervision, large-scale operation and centralized control, could be pointers to future changes in land and landscape in New Zealand. Together with the entry of large joint stock companies and of meat processing and marketing concerns into the livestock farming industries they might well be indicators of impending changes in the rural economy and farm landscape of New Zealand more significant than any that have occurred since the basic patterns of pastoral farming were laid down at the beginning of the century after refrigeration revolutionized farm structures, economies and landscapes.

But the paradox in the case of the Waipaoa plain and the increasingly intensive and efficient use of its naturally fertile soils is that it is surrounded and shut in, except on the seaward side, by hill country in which the use of land is often becoming more extensive, and the roughest and most severely eroded of it is being abandoned, because of the unprecedented and unparalleled devastation caused by soil erosion. Despite the stopbanks, flood protection works and man-made shortcuts for the Waipaoa river in its meanderings over the flats, the plain remains subject to increasing threats as a result of the accelerating run-off and tremendous artificial load of debris carried by its hill country tributaries, especially the Waipaoa and Mangatu above Whatatutu.

Like the inland catchments of other rivers of the East Coast between Gisborne and East Cape – Whakaangiangi, Tapuwaeroa, Kopuapounamu – those of the Mangatu and Te Weraroa tributaries of the Waipaoa are collapsing and crumbling during and after every rainstorm. The catchments are cut into the Cretaceous argillites and shattered early Tertiary bentonitic mudstones and clay shales, in a region occasionally subject to phenomenally high intensity, warm front rains, accentuated by orographic effects, when maritime air masses move in from the east and southeast. Rainfall totals of up to 20 inches in twenty-four hours are not unknown. With the removal of their indigenous cover of mixed rainforest at the turn of the century and the subsequent decay of root anchors, entire hillsides have begun to slide and flow, and rapid and high volume run-off has cut deep gullies on the disrupted poor pasture slopes and deepened the main streams undercutting spurs and base slopes. Now, with every storm, the deeply weathered and saturated regolith moves bodily on every slope in a fantastic display of man-induced forms of mass movement – slips, slides, earth avalanches and mudflows. Large parts of the catchments are sloughing and slurring off the deep mantle of partially weathered soft and greasy rock material, choking valleys with debris and creating temporary lakes. The floors of some valleys have been raised more than 100 feet in fifty years. The devastation first became apparent after the succession of two years of heavy rains in 1916 and 1917. Since then the width of valley floors has doubled and trebled as the lower slopes have been buried deep in a rising tide of grey mud, rubble, silt and decayed logs.

Beside the enormity of this new culturally induced cycle of erosion, the effort of farmers to plant poplars is puny and ineffectual. Much land, blocks up to 8,000 acres in extent, have been abandoned. Access to homesteads is cut off. Roads disappear. Livestock cannot be mustered or shepherded.

The Tarndale 'slip' in the Te Weraroa headwater tributary of the Waipaoa is a frightening sight, and a memorial to the potency of man as an agent in moulding even the physical bases of the landscape in as little as half a century. It reaches now 1,100 yards from the fast-filling bed of the Te Weraroa steeply to the crest of the catchment undermining the Tarndale road along the dividing ridge. Its gullied and contorted, steeply sloping badland surface and adjacent slump scars, slip fractures and rumpled flow surface occupy almost 300 acres.

In the vicinity 17,800 acres of land abandoned for grazing have recently been made available to the New Zealand Forest Service for planting in radiata pine. On the less seriously disturbed and more slowly moving slopes the planting itself has meantime been successful, but whether it can hold the slopes when the next rainfall of expectable ten-year maximum intensity strikes is very doubtful. On the Tarndale 'slip' itself planting is almost impossible. Seedlings would be gullied out by the first rain of quite modest intensity or uprooted and buried

25. Waipaoa headwaters, East Coast
The massive Tarndale slip in the Te Weraroa tributary of the Waipaoa. The whole surface is on the move and the riverbed is rising perceptibly year by year. Soil erosion often occurs on a phenomenal scale in the steep, deforested, rain-drenched hill country of the North Island. Livestock have now been withdrawn from this landscape and experimental planting of thousands of acres of pines is in progress.

in the constant valleyward movement of regolith. With such massive and unaccustomed forms of accelerated erosion, conservation measures must long remain purely experimental. Yet, to some extent in desperation, the New Zealand government has recently decided to undertake, in advance of research, a large-scale conservation programme for the whole East Coast region north of Gisborne.

This involves the use of land already owned by the Crown and administered as state forest land and the acquisition of remote Maori land as well as of privately owned, poor, extensive grazing land in a continuous inland belt, including the upper catchments of all rivers affected by massive scars of man-induced flowage, slippage and gullying. Including the remnant indigenous forest in the highest watersheds, the 'critical headwater area' involves 375,000 acres. Some 236,000 acres is to be planted, mainly in exotic conifers – radiata and Corsican pine and Douglas fir – as dual purpose, protective and productive, forest. The 'pastoral foreland' – 1,185,000 acres of hill country pasture land, extensively used, between the proposed forest belt and the coast – is to be the scene of continued but improved and conservational farm practice. Here the Poverty Bay Catchment Board will be responsible for guiding the introduction of soil conservation practices and encouraging the planting of farm woodlots; and the Department of Agriculture will have the task of improving pastures, grazing management and livestock-carrying capacity.

The afforestation programme begun experimentally in the highly critical problem area in the Mangatu forest in 1959 is to be extended at the rate of 5,000 acres a year. Mangatu in the south will be duplicated in the Tupuwaeroa valley in the north: and both expanded until the critical headwater areas are progressively covered in trees. Within twenty years sawmills and timber treatment plants will be established at Te Karaka, Ruatoria and Hicks Bay; twenty years later still, plywood, veneer, and pulp and paper mills will be required. Meanwhile roads must be built and port facilities improved and extended at both Gisborne and Hicks Bay.

The proposals are to revitalize and reinvigorate and restore the economy, resources and social life of a whole region. If they prove successful they will mark yet another large-scale human transformation of the landscape over hundreds of thousands of acres of New Zealand countryside. They will reverse the course and pattern of man's role in the landscape during the last century and a half. They will replace trees – albeit trees of different and alien species and in uniform and unvarying stands – in regions from which man so ruthlessly and so recklessly and inadvisedly removed them little more than half a century before.

Chapter 9
Small town landscapes

To the casual observer the New Zealand urban scene presents an anomaly. The country's economy is overwhelmingly dependent on the export of agricultural and forest products; the landscape is dominated by extensive areas of green permanent pasture, exotic pine plantations, indigenous stands of forest trees in largely inaccessible mountain country, and large tracts of secondary forest growth in hill country areas once crudely and hurriedly cleared but now reverting as slope, rainfall and erosion proved that some areas were too unstable and difficult for permanent pastures. Yet despite this heavy dependence on the soil and its products the country is highly urbanized – 77 per cent of the population live in towns and cities with populations in excess of 1,000 people. Not only is New Zealand highly urbanized but the urban population has low residential densities. Thus the extent of the urban landscape is still larger than the casual observer would expect.

Such a situation, in which a rural economy prevails yet where a high degree of urbanization has developed, is not confined to New Zealand. Several of the younger countries in the western world have the same characteristic. Those countries which were settled by Europeans within the last two centuries have been able to take advantage of new technologies in farm production, management and marketing making it possible to attain greatly increased rural production with decreased manpower. Fewer and fewer are directly employed on the land and more and more of the labour force is engaged in processing farm and forest products but especially in providing a wide range of services to maintain the efficiency of the rural economy.

In New Zealand, these innovations have led to high levels of *per capita* production in agriculture and forestry, and a corresponding close grid of country towns has developed to provide the essential services demanded and required by a rural economy in an economically productive and affluent society.

Falling within the same size category as the country towns, but fewer in number, are the generally much more recent towns which have sprung up alongside and in association with major development works or large exploitive industries. Such towns include those founded on the exploitation of coal resources, on construction projects associated with the development of the country's power resources, and those created to serve the needs of the growing timber industry and its allied trades. Although they fall within the same

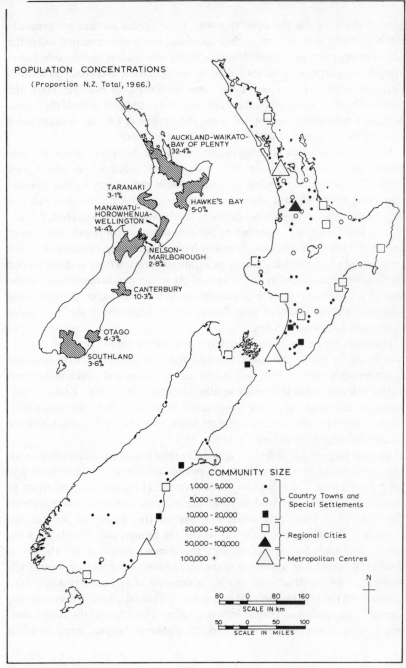

POPULATION CONCENTRATIONS
(Proportion N.Z. Total, 1966.)

AUCKLAND-WAIKATO-
BAY OF PLENTY
32.4%

TARANAKI
3.1%

HAWKE'S BAY
5.0%

MANAWATU-
HOROWHENUA-
WELLINGTON
14.4%

NELSON-
MARLBOROUGH
2.8%

CANTERBURY
10.3%

OTAGO
4.3%

SOUTHLAND
3.6%

COMMUNITY SIZE

- 1,000 - 5,000
○ 5,000 - 10,000
■ 10,000 - 20,000
□ 20,000 - 50,000
▲ 50,000 - 100,000
△ 100,000 +

Country Towns and
Special Settlements

Regional Cities

Metropolitan Centres

N

SCALE IN km
80   0   80   160

SCALE IN MILES
50   0   50   100

26. *Urban landscapes*

143

general size range as the country towns, these special settlements generally differ markedly in their form, in their social and functional structure, and in the nature of their ties, links and relations with the surrounding countryside. However, the country towns and special urban centres do not necessarily have functions always mutually exclusive: the same town may, for example, house the miners who work in the pits some miles away and in addition provide the farmer with his weekly shopping requirements, the services of a livestock agent and a railhead for the movement of his livestock and fertilizer.

Despite the fact that both the country town and the special centre are intimately linked with the major rural and primary industries on which New Zealand's economy is founded, the proportion of the country's urban population living within them is small. In fact, 60 per cent of the urban population lives in the four metropolitan centres of Auckland, Wellington-Hutt, Christchurch and Dunedin.* A further 24 per cent of the urban population lives in the other thirteen urban areas, all of which have populations in excess of 20,000 persons and all of which are dominant within a regional setting as major service centres. This leaves a mere 16 per cent of the urban population housed in the smaller settlements – those with populations of less than 20,000 persons, those which serve rural industries most directly and which make up the lower order of the urban settlement fabric.

However, regardless of the relatively small proportion of the urban population living in them, the country towns and special centres have assumed characteristics which reflect their origin and functions and which make them an intrinsic and characteristically significant element in the New Zealand landscape. In their appearance, the combination of activities that take place within them, and the people who live and work there, they display features which are peculiarly indigenous to New Zealand.

Because they tend to differ in origin and in their functional relationships with the surrounding rural area the two types of settlement – country town and special settlement – are here treated separately. However, it is important to remember that these two kinds of settlement are both intimately concerned with the country's primary production and together they house the forester, the miner and the construction worker, service the farmer, and provide the most regular and frequent contact between the primary producer and the urban dweller. Whether it be a member of the high country squattocracy, a construction worker on a hydroelectric dam in the remote and wild countryside, a dairy farmer from the neat and ordered farmscape of Taranaki, a coal miner from the exposed rain-sodden and forest-hemmed valleys and ridges of the West Coast, or a gang of Maori shearers or fencers, all require and expect access to urban

* There are eighteen defined urban areas but for present purposes the administratively separate but physically contiguous areas of Wellington and Hutt have been grouped together.

facilities to supply their varied day-to-day needs in order to do their jobs efficiently.

The country towns' most intimate function is to provide the regular requirements of the primary producer. The frequency of their occurrence and the size they attain tend to reflect the kind of farming in the areas around them. On the other hand, most of the country towns are as old as the areas they serve so that their present distribution may also be an indication of the factors influencing town development about the time at which they were founded. Subsequent changes in road and rail networks, and in the forms and efficiency of transport, resulting in increased accessibility to larger centres, would today render many existing country towns redundant under contemporary conditions, but traditional associations between town and district, allegiance to local traders and professional services, habit and inertia, community identification and interest have all contributed to preserving the existence of most country towns in the pattern in which they first appeared.

The country town in New Zealand is characteristically a small rural service centre. Its population falls within the range of from 1,000 to 20,000 persons. Over four-fifths of the towns have populations of less than 6,000 and the great bulk of them are within the range of from 1,000 to 4,000 people.

Most of the towns are at the intersection of a main road with more important secondary roads leading into their hinterlands. Areas where more intensive agriculture is practised, where farm units are smaller, and where the rural population densities are highest, show the greatest regularity in the spacing and size of their towns. In the South Island, the livestock fattening and crop economies of the Canterbury and Southland plains illustrate a certain regularity in the distribution of the country towns over the lowlands. In the North Island, the Waikato, Bay of Plenty and Taranaki areas, and the Wanganui, Manawatu and Horowhenua coastal strip are like the Canterbury and Southland plains in revealing a number of regular patterns of service centre distribution.

The regularity of spacing and size can be illustrated by reference to the Waikato-Hauraki plains lowland. This is an area where dairying is dominant and where factories processing cream and milk dot the landscape. Parts of the area have been farmed for the last hundred years and other parts for fifty years. During that time a close grid of roads has developed, linking the now relatively high density rural population (generally more than twenty persons per square mile) with the towns. In this area a cluster of country towns is focused on the regional centre of Hamilton (63,303 in 1966). With almost regimented precision, the city's satellites are spaced at from thirteen to twenty miles from each other. For example, it is twenty miles from Hamilton to Morrinsville (4,497); thirteen miles from Morrinsville to Te Aroha (3,212); thirteen from Te Aroha to Paeroa (3,129); thirteen from Paeroa to Waihi (3,169); twenty from Te Aroha to Matamata (3,810); twenty from Matamata to Putaruru (4,435); twenty from

Hamilton to Huntly (5,401); twenty from Hamilton to Te Awamutu (6,719); thirteen from Hamilton to Cambridge (5,962); thirteen from Cambridge to Te Awamutu; twenty from Cambridge to Matamata, and so on. In addition, numerous smaller villages are spaced along the roads between the service centres further punctuating the road distances between the towns. These villages, with from 200 to 500 people, most often find their *raison d'être* in the presence of a small dairy or cheese factory such as those found at Tatuanui, Tirau, Hinuera, Bruntwood and numerous others. A similar exercise could be carried out on the spacing and size of towns such as Hawera, Stratford, Eltham, Patea, Marton, Feilding, Shannon and Otaki on the western littoral of Taranaki and southwards to Wellington, and in the South Island for centres like Oxford, Rangiora, Kaiapoi, Methven, Geraldine, Ashburton and Temuka.

Where the spacing is less predictable and the size of service centres less regular, a change in the type or intensity of activity in the hinterland is indicated. Other factors which obviously affect the distribution pattern include the size and shape of the hinterland; the time at which the area was developed; and the relationship of the service centre to a regional or metropolitan city.

But despite the variations which occur in size and spacing, the rural service centres throughout the country have an almost monotonous and predictable similarity of appearance and function that makes it possible to erect a hypothetical or model 'Kiwitown' of perhaps 2,500 people, which provides a generalized replica or example which comes close to describing all such towns in reality.

Kiwitown is found on a crossroad with the main highway forming its major axis. This feature has moulded the basic form of the town with its retail core strung along the main street through which is channelled all passing traffic. It also provides kerbside parking for local shoppers. From this main thoroughfare a rectangular pattern of streets forming a grid makes up the outline of the rest of the built-up area and of the area laid out in streets but not yet fully built on.

After traversing miles of open farmland today's motorist finds that Kiwitown beckons first in a scatter of billboards beside the highway. It is heralded by a few isolated houses backed by grassy farm paddocks, a cemetery, a scatter of industrial buildings including a general engineering workshop, a noisy panel beating shed, farm machinery maintenance yards filled with old tractors and secondhand farm implements, a concrete pipes and posts factory. Finally, a continuous border of houses and then the commercial strip proper marks his arrival in Kiwitown.

Within the town the main street is faced by an assortment of buildings and styles of architecture. A low profile made up of single-storey structures – many with false wooden fronts carrying the name and nature of the existing or former occupier or original owner – an irregular collection of two-storeyed

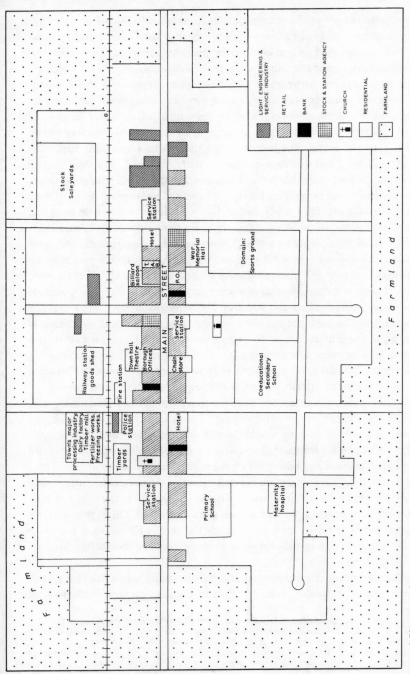

27. 'Kiwitown'

concrete units with professional rooms and, occasionally, living quarters up-stairs, a large, solid brick or stone-built town hall, a hotel or two, and a miscel-lany of buildings used for non-commercial purposes. Almost all the commercial buildings have verandahs projecting over the footpaths – verandahs which are constructed of rusty corrugated iron with ornamentally decorated barge boards and from which are draped canvas awnings or new, straight and severe struc-tures. All this protrusion results in an assortment of sizes and heights, of verandahs, struts, and downpipes. Advertising signs add to the visual confusion.

The range of commercial uses is wide – the general retail store, hardware, furniture, fabrics and sportsgoods shops, a dairy/milkbar,* tea rooms, a small restaurant or grill room, barber and hairdressing salon, and shoe shops com-prise the basic store types. This list is supplemented by chemists' and jewellers' shops, banks, post office, stock and station agencies which handle farm real estate, equipment, stock sales and finance, and a chain store of the Woolworth's variety. In addition, regardless of size, there are other 'institutional' activities which are ubiquitous – the TAB agency (Totalizer Agency Board office at which townsfolk and farmfolk place off-course bets on horse races), billiard saloon, licensed hotel or pub (either old, two-storeyed and wooden with a long second-floor balcony overlooking the street or a new single-storeyed brick and tile structure), the borough council offices and a picture theatre (both of which may be separate establishments or housed in the town hall), at least two service stations and perhaps a veterinary club. Some commercial development has expanded a short distance into several of the adjacent side streets and here also are found the police station, volunteer fire brigade and ambulance depot.

Parallel to the main street and within a short distance of it, the railway line has created another functional grouping of land uses; the station itself, the goods shed with its splitting weatherboards and fading red paint, timber yards and a bulk store for fertilizer. In addition, stock pens alongside the livestock saleyards, thronged and noisy only on the regular weekly or monthly sale days and deserted between times, are normally close to the railway line and station yards. Kiwitown has a dairy factory. This too has access to the railway siding to forward the finished product to cool store and wharf. Other towns have a freezing works or timber mill. Just outside the core of Kiwitown is a modern factory established since 1945 employing female labour on the machine produc-tion of clothing.

Other institutional buildings found in Kiwitown include a primary school, a coeducational secondary school, a Roman Catholic convent and school, an

---

* The 'dairy' is a feature of a New Zealand shopping street as universal and indigenous as the drug-store in the USA. It is found also as the most indispensable unit in every neighbourhood shopping centre of metropolitan suburbs. It is primarily a shop selling milk, eggs, butter, confectionery, newspapers and bread but it may also have provision for light meals and stock a limited range of groceries and frozen foods. It remains open to customers late in the evening and on Saturdays and Sundays.

28. '*Kiwitown*' *(in this case, Gore, Southland)*
Service centre for much of the rural farm community of the rich livestock farming areas of Southland, Gore has a population of 8,280. Its main street is wider than usual but the facades and structure of its buildings are representative.

RSA (Returned Servicemen's Association clubrooms), and a war memorial hall built in remembrance of the servicemen killed in either or both world wars.

The disposition and pattern of the residential area in Kiwitown summarize the history of the town's development. It is best recorded in the variety of housing styles. The early colonial house in the main street or in close proximity to it, with lean-to verandah along its front and a door set exactly in the middle of the front wall, framed by two large sash windows, awaits its takeover by commercial or industrial uses. The villa, with its ornate fretworked scallops both around the verandah and along the gable barge boards, stained glass enclosing one end of the verandah, and a high pitched gable to the front room, was much in vogue up to the 1920s. The villas, too, are found close to the main street. The bungalow with casement windows, curved window boxes, single gabled roof of lower pitch – a generally more substantial and larger dwelling – was popular in the late 1920s through World War II. Finally, the post World War II growth of Kiwitown is measurable in the number of brick veneer, artificial stone or narrow

149

weatherboarded houses of various shapes and sizes, comprising the rest of the built-up area. A few state houses, some in a cul-de-sac, and built in the immediate postwar period are clearly recognizable from their regimented positioning on sections and from their high-pitched tile roofs, small windows and concrete stucco or weatherboard construction. Railway houses and houses built by the dairy factory are equally distinctive in their similarity of design, uniform colour schemes, institutional numbering and in their location close to the installations they serve.

Kiwitown is a busy settlement. The regular sale day brings the largest influx of farmers and their wives. They come by truck or car with trailer so that they can combine farm business, the transport of stock or supplies, the opportunity of consulting accountants, stock agents and contractors about jobs on the farm, and shopping by the women. Late night shopping on Friday evening is another time when the streets are thronged with young and old making purchases, window shopping and meeting people along the footpaths which readily become cluttered with groups discussing the week's events or the sporting fixture for the day following. Each morning and evening buses from the rural area arrive and depart carrying young women from farms and smaller settlements to their shop and office and factory employment while special school buses travel round the hinterland collecting and delivering pupils to the secondary school in town.

The town is linked to its hinterland – and dependent on it for its growth – by a fabric woven from commercial, educational and social fibres. Deliveries by retailers once, twice or three times a week and involving distances of up to 100 miles on each trip, are a major part of the services provided for farm families. Postal deliveries by the rural mail van forge yet another contact between town and farm. The local weekly newspaper together with metropolitan or regional dailies delivered by the 'maily' keep both urban and rural dweller informed of the events in their district and in the country at large. Sporting affiliations – the rugby, golf and tennis clubs – and organizations such as Rotary, Red Cross and Women's Institute foster additional community activities.

The extent of the hinterland is largely dependent on the location and proximity of competing centres, on the shape and surface configuration of the hinterland, and on the nature of the rural activities within it. A crude measure indicates that the country town probably serves a population at least as large as that contained within the town itself. In more intensive agricultural areas the dispersed rural population approaches twice the size of that of the town serving it.

The monotonous replication of the country town's general characteristics is relieved in individual instances by the thoughtful designation of a domain or careful development of a park, by trees lining the streets, or by the efforts of one of the many service organizations in providing a pleasant roadside stopping place with seats and tables for travellers. But this, above all, is the place where the farmer feels equally at home dressed in his working garb of black bush singlet, blue denims, hobnailed boots or mud-spattered gum boots or in his formal clothes with the brim of his hat turned down all round, sports coat and unaccustomed tie; where a gang of shearers or fencers – Maori or *pakeha* – stop in their old pre-war car or truck for a meal or a beer on their way north, south, east or west to the next contract; where a farm tractor in the main street is just as acceptable and will draw less attention from those lounging on the footpaths than the latest model car. So, too, the double-decked sheep truck, the cattle truck and trailer, the tractor with farm machinery in tow, the stainless steel articulated bulk milk tanker, the manure truck, the saleyards and the dairy factory, the seed store, the wheat or maize silos, the flour mill, the displays of new and secondhand ploughing, discing, silagemaking, harvesting and threshing machinery, all in different combinations emphasize the role that 'Kiwitowns' throughout New Zealand play in providing services to the agricultural communities.

The special settlement differs in many respects from the country towns. Instead of providing a range of services to an external community living in the surrounding hinterland, it performs functions primarily for its own population and houses within it the workforce engaged on some particular specialized enterprise or commercialized exploitation. In addition, these settlements are much more closely orientated to a single resource so that their distribution is much more irregular and variable – Deniston, Stockton and Benneydale to coal reserves; Cromwell, Clyde and Naseby to worked out gold deposits; Mangakino and Matahina and Roxburgh to the harnessing of water power; Wairakei to geothermal steam bores; Owhanga and Mamaku to indigenous forest stands, and Murupara and Kinleith to plantations of exotic trees; Wanaka, Queenstown and Russell to scenery, historic associations and fishing attractions.

Because their existence is tied to specific resources, the number of people in these towns is a much clearer reflection of the size of a single industrial enterprise. It may vary from a few hundred to 5,000 or 6,000 persons. Kawerau and Tokoroa have populations of 5,800 and 8,800 respectively while the dead or declining coal and gold mining centres of the South Island – Naseby (150), Arrowtown (180), Kumara (420) and Nightcaps (710) – still retain their formal borough status though their population has long since declined to less than 1,000, if it ever reached that number. Two tourist centres, Queenstown and Russell, have populations of 1,400 and 500 respectively. And the structure of the population of the special settlements frequently deviates more from the New Zealand urban norm than does that of other nucleations. Only the single man and the young married couples seek out and are attracted to today's new towns with their high wages, overtime and cheap housing, to compensate for the frequent lack of a wide range of facilities normally found in towns of equivalent size. Only the older folk cling to houses in declining mining areas where coal has been superseded by other fuels and where employment opportunities in the industry are limited.

The special settlements can be divided into two basic groups: those which are permanent, or at least as permanent as the resources on which they are based; and those which are temporary and have a fixed life of perhaps only a few years. There is, however, one feature common to both. Because the exploitation of a particular resource generally requires the application of capital, equipment and personnel almost simultaneously, the vast majority of the settlements are created in a short time. Whether it be gold, coal, timber, water or steam, the initial build-up is rapid and subsequent expansion slow, so that few of them reveal the slow evolution of the country towns. They are thus more individual in their appearance and it is not possible to erect a model, the equivalent of a Kiwitown, to describe them. Building styles, for example, are fixed by the fashion at the time of the settlement's inception and little further change or addition has normally taken place. The settlement, complete with whatever range of facilities and services it was to have, appeared almost literally overnight. For this reason it often retains an atmosphere and a limited set of relationships with the surrounding rural area which mark it off as alien within the predominantly rural landscape.

Because it is based on a single major enterprise which houses and employs most of its residents, the special settlement has close affinities with the company town which is dependent on the activities of one solitary employer. Within the New Zealand context, the company is often substituted by a government department – forestry, electricity or mines – although large private enterprise establishments are once more becoming increasingly significant in creating special towns associated with forestry and other exploitive activities.

There was no one particular period at which special settlements were established on the New Zealand scene. They have occurred almost throughout the whole span of the country's economic and urban history. The oldest form derives from the gold and coal mining settlements of the last century and the timber milling communities which were set up as soon as the colonists realized the rich potential harboured in the vast stands of New Zealand's indigenous bush. The most recent are those associated with the integrated timber, pulp and paper industries of the central North Island, and with the exploitation of New Zealand's power resources at Wairakei (geothermal steam), on the Waikato, Rangitaiki, Waitaki and Clutha rivers and at Lake Manapouri.

In general, the gold mining centres were purely ephemeral. As the pioneer individual or small parties of miners probed into the interior basins and along the gorges and terraces of the Otago Province and the river valleys of the West Coast, news of a rich strike would bring a stampede of thousands in their wake. Material comforts were unimportant compared with the possibility of overnight riches. Rough-hewn planks and calico tents provided shelter. Formed streets and paving were unknown in the boom days of Naseby, Cromwell, Shotover and Hokitika. Grog shops, crude supplies of foodstuffs and picks, shovels and pans were the essentials of the miner's needs. Coaches over rutted shingle tracks and partly formed 'roads' and coastal vessels to the mouths of rivers provided sufficient transport.

Only in places such as the Karangahake Gorge near Waihi, Waihi itself, and Thames, where large sophisticated batteries were required to crush the quartz-bearing rock, did any semblance of greater permanence appear. Sustained and systematic mining over a lengthy period gave rise to small mining centres such

29. *Cromwell, Central Otago*

Hemmed in by faulted schist mountain slopes and gravel terraces flooring the graben, Cromwell (pop. 1,090) sits on a terrace above the junction of the Clutha and Kawarau rivers. Its origin and growth go back to gold mining days. Its present function is to service small fruit-growing and high country pastoral grazing communities. It also has some holiday traffic. Its 'commercial core' is immediately across the bridge over the Clutha. In the foreground is the rail terminus and railway housing. The gravel piles, upper right, are the tailings of a gold dredge.

as MacKay Town, Waikino and Karangahake perched on the walls of the gorge or tucked in valleys tributary to it. But many contemporary towns of medium sizes – Hokitika, Coromandel, Thames, Waihi, and Alexandra – received their initial impetus from the concentration of miners, from the pubs and general merchants, from the assayer's office, police station, coach house and stables provided to service mushrooming mining communities. When the frenzied search for gold around such towns ebbed, their basic framework remained. Most people shifted away but a few entrepreneurs and residents remained and, in favourable locations, built the town up again as agriculture developed in the rural areas and gave it a less spectacular but more sustained basis of existence.

But many were not so fortunate as to experience the subsequent development of another activity capable of supporting them once the gold had gone. Within a few years the gorse and grass and aggressive indigenous scrub reasserted their right to the site and scores of urban places, born during the gold rushes, became derelict, and faded into obscurity. Only the drifts and shafts and piles of rubble, rusted equipment and a few crumbling buildings today litter verdant landscapes as reminders of former urban forms of occupance.

The coal mining towns, on the other hand, have had a longer life largely because the process of extraction has called for much longer term development and an organized workforce. In the South Island, the coal reserves of the West Coast and of Otago-Southland were probed after the gold rushes so that the former gold mining centres of Greymouth and Westport were granted a new lease of life. The Waikato coal deposits near Taupiri and west of Huntly were also developed before the turn of the century.

Most mining was underground in the early years and drifts were driven into the hillsides. Only a few shaft mines were developed – at Huntly and Kaitangata. The minehead features were remarkably unimpressive – a small tunnel entrance with narrow gauge rail tracks to carry the skips in and out of the mine clipped to an endless wire rope, stables for the horses which were used underground, a tally cabin, weighbridge, mine office, explosives store and bathhouse. Dilapidated wooden and corrugated iron huts were tucked into the fold of a hillside and largely hidden from view. A rope-road from the mine to the screens at a convenient railhead cut across the country or plunged down the steep hillside from the mines perched high above the valleys of Westland.

The small scatter of mean and crude houses close by the pithead developed into small mining villages at places like Renown, McDonald, Rotowaro, Pukemiro and Glen Afton on the fields west of Huntly and at Blackball, Stockton, Granity, Ngakawa and Runanga on the West Coast, Nightcaps and Ohai in Southland, and Kamo in Northland. But early in the development, many of the miners chose to live in the larger centres of Huntly, Westport and Greymouth, and Whangarei, and to travel daily to the outlying mines by train and later by bus. Many of the smaller villages are now being deserted as the mines are closed or are reaching the end of their economic life and as more and more of those miners remaining prefer to live in the larger towns.

Since 1945 opencast mining has become much more economic and now a handful of men and modern machinery can produce more coal than the hundreds who previously carried out the much more hazardous task underground. But the opencasts at Huntly and at Maramarua are much more destructive landscape agents – piles of overburden, stripped to reveal the coal seam, are stacked in great mounds, bare, unconsolidated and unvegetated to be washed downhill in the first heavy rainfall and to clog and discolour streams and creeks. Lakes have been systematically drained to reach the coal measures and infilled after the fuel has been won.

In the primary centres of coal mining today – Westport, Greymouth and Huntly – there is little obvious sign that mining has been, or is, the main prop of the town. Most have developed additional services to cater for the farming communities which developed around them and they now have many of the essential features of the country towns. Only the wagons of coal in the shunting yards, the daily departure of bus loads of miners going off to the pits, and the roar of diesel trucks carting coal from the opencasts indicate significant differences.

Most obvious and most specialized of the contemporary settlements are those associated with the development of the country's power resources and with its forests and forest industries. Two modern or recent special settlements, Te Mahoe and Kawerau, have been selected to illustrate some of the major characteristics of such centres. Both are less than fifteen years old – one is permanent, the other has already passed through its peak period of development and only a small nucleation of permanent dwellings and a massive earth dam remain. Both are engaged in harnessing the resources of the central North Island – Kawerau, the scene of an integrated timber, pulp and paper industry tapping the vast manmade Kaingaroa forest; Te Mahoe, the construction town for a large earth dam harnessing the waters of the Rangitaiki river to produce power for the national grid.

Te Mahoe was not the first such hydro-power construction town – nor is it likely to be the last. Already the countryside has seen the rise and decline of a number of these towns – Roxburgh on the Clutha, Otematata on the Waitaki, Mangakino on the Waikato, Wairakei on the geothermal steam zone close to the Waikato, and Meremere south of Mercer fed by the coal from the Maramarua opencast. One author who lived and worked in such a town summed up its life cycle in the following way:

In 1946 the site upon which Roxburgh hydro was built could boast only bare rocks and windswept hills, but by 1953 there lay spread over one square mile, the biggest and most modern settlement in Central Otago. By 1957, the dam was almost finished and most of the residents had left to seek fortunes elsewhere. When a move was made from Roxburgh to Benmore [another dam project but on the Waitaki not the Clutha], 73 miles in a straight line to the northeast, only a maintenance village together with the remnants of the old construction town were left.*

Te Mahoe followed much the same sequence. In 1959, after four years of site testing and investigation the Matahina dam project was granted approval and the construction town of Te Mahoe came into existence seven miles south of Te Teko. By mid-1967, the project was virtually completed and the village was being run down; the equipment, houses and men required for the next project were in the process of being shifted; those houses, huts and other buildings no longer needed were to be auctioned to the public; those employees who did not seek or accept transfer to another project were looking for jobs elsewhere. All that now remain are the twenty-four neat and ordered brick and tile houses of the New Zealand Electricity Department's permanent staff and a hostel to accommodate a few single people and any additional technical personnel who may be required at the site for short periods. This small permanent nucleation, duplicated at every one of New Zealand's twenty-two hydro dam sites, is on a small cul-de-sac tucked in below the shelter of the dam. Yet over a period of a few short years Te Mahoe was a thriving community of 4,500 persons, housed and serviced for the sole task of constructing a dam. A community which was, in effect, self-contained and semi-isolated from the community of dairy farmers in the lower Rangitaiki valley; a community which was transitory and mobile but one which can be found at any time somewhere in New Zealand; a community which, regardless of location, not only looks the same but is almost literally made up of the same houses, huts and personnel. The hydro construction workers are almost the modern New Zealand equivalent of the gypsy.

Te Mahoe was built on two terrace levels downstream from the dam site. On the lower terrace level nearest the river where the sewerage treatment plant and the single men's camp. Overlooking the camp on a small embankment to the south was the Ministry of Works' staff hostel which not only provided accommodation for the single male staff but also provided mess facilities for the single women (staff appointees) whose flats were immediately opposite the hostel.

On the upper terrace level, the northern section – that most distant from the dam site – was developed with temporary housing for married workers. At the southern end of the terrace were the houses of the senior Ministry of Works' staff, the school houses, school and the new permanent village of the New Zealand Electricity Department.

---

* W. J. CAMPBELL, *Hydrotown*, Dunedin 1957.

The single men's camp was clearly recognizable by the regimented lines of 12 by 10 foot huts grouped into blocks, each block having its own ablution facilities. The blocks, in turn, were grouped around a central kitchen and mess hall. The camp was also provided with a 'dry' canteen and a recreation hall, and was thus physically and socially divorced from the remainder of the village. The Ministry of Works' single men's staff hostel was superior in design and had a choicer site than the camp. Here a social club room was also provided with a 'wet' canteen.

The quarters for married workers were laid out on sealed streets but the dominating characteristic was the smallness and boxlike design of the houses. These houses are transportable and are moved from project to project as required. Indeed, the slight variation in design among the houses carried the designation of the project at which they were first used. At Te Mahoe there were three basic house types – the Meremere style, the Mangakino style, and the Sullivan style (the latter named after the person who designed it rather than an earlier project site). Basically, all the houses were two-bedroomed and if the family which inhabited one such dwelling was too large, the required number of 10 by 10 foot huts were placed on the section to provide extra bedrooms. The Ministry of Works' married staff were provided with somewhat larger houses which had been built on the site.

In addition to the different units of accommodation making up the settlement, provision was made for a small service centre. This comprised a shop, post office, library, primary school, medical clinic, police station, a large hall which could be used for films, a smaller social hall, and a small building in which committees and clubs could meet.

From the time the project got under way in 1959 until May 1967, 2,590 men had been employed on the project although at the peak period of construction the workforce totalled about 780 men. These figures hold the key to much of the character of such settlements. There is, inevitably, a high turnover of labour during the short history of the project – especially among the single men. In addition, such a project requires different skills at different stages of construction so that there is considerable shuffling of workmen from project to project as their specialist trades are needed. This constant change of people at the site and in the village emphasizes the temporary nature of the settlement. Some residents go to the trouble of developing gardens and personalizing their homes, but overall the short-term nature of the project and the even shorter-term stay of many of its residents drapes the village in a monotonous, unkempt, dusty, drab, frequently noisy, and transient atmosphere which emphasizes its fate never to mature.

In contrast to the temporary character of Te Mahoe, Kawerau is a new town, but one with an established and recognizable future. The town is on the flood plain of the Tarawera river, huddled beneath the domineering, bare and treeless volcanic cone of Mount Edgecumbe and surrounded on three sides by subdued and gently rounded knolls of ash-covered farmland at the head of the Rangitaiki plains. In the early 1950s, Kawerau existed only as a blueprint on the drawing boards in the office of the Town and Country Planning Branch of the Ministry of Works, Wellington. In less than a decade it had gained the status of a borough and in 1966 had reached a population of 5,826.

The town has been laid out on a formalized plan. The majority of the private homes have been set on one-eighth of an acre sections. Approximately half the dwellings in the borough have been built by the state. The dominance of state houses with their limited variations in design, orientation and placement on the sections, contributes to the feeling that the town lacks variety. Two elements offset the uniformity of the residential area. First, nearly all the homes have well-

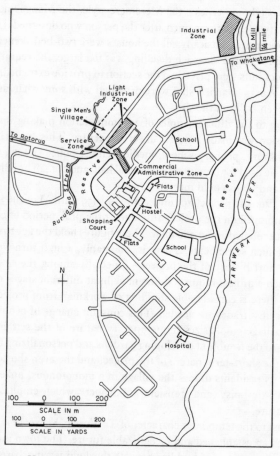

30. *Kawerau: special settlement*

tended lawns and gardens, which indicates that many of the residents consider themselves permanent inhabitants and not just transients who will move on to the next job when the present one is completed – an attitude which prevails in the temporary towns. Secondly, the homes of the mill executives and of an increasing number of other members of the community are situated on a small elevated terrace of the Tarawera river about 20 to 30 feet above the uniform level of the remainder of the town. On the whole, the houses on 'nob hill' are much larger, more expensive, and certainly more varied in design than the houses elsewhere in Kawerau. In addition, a staff hostel in the centre of the town and a single men's village characteristically on the perimeter of the borough provide further contrasts in the residential area.

The greater part of the town has been laid out in semicircular shape and is centred on a modern shopping court. The court constitutes the business section of Kawerau and is characterized by its low profile – only one establishment being more than single-storeyed – its provision of off-street parking, service lanes for heavy-vehicle access to the rear of retail units, and its lawns and paths connecting the shops. Zoning has been rigidly implemented so that retail, commercial, service, industrial, administrative and residential functions are clearly and sometimes artificially defined.

In the same way that Mount Edgecumbe dominates the town in the physical sense, so the timber, pulp and paper mill dominates it in an economic and social sense. If the wind blows from the east the penetrating smell from the processing of wood chips and pulp permeates the town. The mill operates twenty-four hours a day, seven days a week. Shift work affects the whole regime of the town. The plant is fed by five regular daily trainloads of pine logs from Murupara, headquarters of the Kaingaroa Logging Company, by vast quantities of water drawn from the fast-flowing Tarawera river, and by geothermal steam which has been tapped on the site and which provides both power and heat for drying during processing. Regular shipments of sawn timber, sulphate pulp and paper are railed from the plant to the new port of Mount Maunganui for export, or are trucked and railed to markets in New Zealand. The degree of integration, the capital invested, the size of the workforce employed, and the value of output all make this a very large operation by New Zealand standards. Great piles of logs, mountainous heaps of chips awaiting processing, the shuttle of trains, the whine of power saws, the roar from an uncapped geothermal bore belching clouds of steam, the regular movement of shift workers between home and plant, stacks of sawn timber, the constant movement of gantry cranes stacking products, and the sulphurous and resin odours are all essential elements of one of New Zealand's major export industries at full production.

Two further features of Kawerau are characteristic of many of New Zealand's new special settlements. Because of the short time since the town's establishment and the structure of the workforce, the composition of its population is atypical by New Zealand urban standards. Kawerau's population, like that of other similar settlements, is dominated by a high proportion of males. This is particularly so because of the large numbers of single men who are attracted by the high wages associated with shift work and by the provision of accommodation. The population is also very young. Few elderly people take part in this modern form of urban pioneering. As in the construction towns, the turnover of labour in such special settlements may be high. Again, this is largely the result of the large component of single men. But for the family man, too, employment of his youngsters in jobs other than those provided by the Company presents problems, and many families are forced or prefer to shift as their children reach the school leaving age. But in contrast to Te Mahoe, lawns and gardens are established, local organizations supported, and permanent residence is the intention, if not the act, of most of its people.

The dominance of the Tasman Pulp and Paper Company as employer, landlord and general benefactor in the town can become an additional source of irritation. Many of the special settlements founded on a single enterprise – especially those which are temporary – lack an independent form of local government, although Kawerau does not fall completely within this category. Kawerau has a town council but it is only partly elected. Its other members are appointed representatives of the company.

Mention has already been made of the limited relationships which often exist between the new town and the older established rural community about it. This is partly due to the locational attributes of the particular resources on which many of the towns are based. Obviously the forest settlement of Kaingaroa, surrounded by tall timber stands stretching for miles in every direction has no other role to play apart from housing and servicing the forestry community living there. But where rural communities and special towns are in juxtaposition as at Kawerau, Murupara and Mangakino, there is frequently little contact between the two. This is often the result of an association previously established by the rural community with other towns long before the special centre appeared. It is also often the result of a lack in the new town of services and facilities geared to a farming community. Stock and station agencies, saleyards, engineering works, fertilizer stocks, veterinary services are usually not present to attract the farmer away from the traditional centres where these needs are satisfied.

The new town of Turangi, which now succeeds Te Mahoe as the construction centre of New Zealand's junior 'Snowy Mountain' scheme – the Tongariro power development – is designed with a different aim in view. The town which has been built for the scheme was designed and planned on a much more permanent basis in the hope that when the construction workers disperse at the completion of the project, the business core and services will remain not only to meet the needs of the permanent workforce at the dam but also to act as a service centre for the rapidly developing rural areas which surround it and as a tourist resort on the southern shores of Lake Taupo.

The steady and continuous growth of the traditional country towns and the often spectacular growth of the special settlements are both healthy signs of economic progress in the primary sector of the New Zealand economy. Both service an important section of the country's population and are extremely vital components in the settled and established agricultural landscapes and in the more recent landscapes man is shaping in the wild country or in newly developed and exploited areas such as the Volcanic Plateau.

Chapter 10
City landscapes

The four metropolitan centres – Auckland, Wellington-Hutt, Christchurch and Dunedin – dominate New Zealand's social and political life. Sixty per cent of the total urban population lives in these four urban areas. For certain specialized activities the sphere of influence of each of these cities ranges over the whole country, but for more general goods and services their spacing has led to a division of the country into four primary hinterlands. Auckland serves the northern half of the North Island, while Wellington commands its southern portion and the Nelson-Marlborough area of the South Island. Christchurch's metropolitan influence extends south from the southern boundary of the Nelson-Marlborough area and includes the greater part of the West Coast, while Dunedin takes in the remainder of the South Island.

The actual size of the four centres and their recent growth rates are indicative of significant differences in the progress and productivity of their respective hinterlands. They also point to contrasts in the character and dynamics of their respective urban landscapes. Auckland is by far the largest of the four (548,293 in 1966) and has been growing more rapidly than the other three over the last fifty years. The Wellington-Hutt area (282,487) is also expanding rapidly while Christchurch (247,248) grew at approximately half the rate of Auckland during the last intercensal period, 1961–66. Dunedin (108,734) has for several decades now shown little sign of active growth and can be regarded as virtually stagnant compared with the other major cities and some of its competitors from the ranks of the regional cities.

These differences in the size of the four main centres and the variations in the intensity of the productivity of their hinterlands are further emphasized when their satellites, the regional cities, are considered. Auckland has five such cities within its hinterland. They have a total population of 185,400. In addition, four of the five cities – Whangarei (29,500), Hamilton (63,300), Rotorua (32,200) and Tauranga (31,600) experienced higher rates of growth during the 1961–66 intercensal period than did Auckland itself. The fifth city, Gisborne (27,800), is strictly peripheral to Auckland's influence and should perhaps be regarded as falling within the spheres of both Wellington and Auckland. Gisborne increased its population by 10·9 per cent (1961–66) which placed it twelfth among the seventeen cities and metropolitan centres in terms of rate of growth.

Wellington has within its sphere of influence six regional cities with an aggregate population of 225,700 persons. Palmerston North (49,100), New Plymouth (35,200), Napier (38,300), Hastings (37,400) and Wanganui (38,100) are in the North Island, while Nelson (27,600) commands that northern portion of the South Island which lies within Wellington's sphere of influence. With the exception of New Plymouth, Wanganui and Nelson, the regional cities in this area showed large intercensal increases.

In marked contrast to the two North Island primary cities, those in the South Island, Christchurch and Dunedin, have each only one regional city within their respective hinterlands. In the case of Christchurch, Timaru (27,900) showed the least intercensal increase of all the cities in this class. Dunedin's regional city, Invercargill (46,000), has been growing quite rapidly over the last few decades as the chief town and port of the Southland plains. In the next decade Invercargill could become the fastest growing urban area in the country, when the waters from the Manapouri scheme are harnessed and the electricity generated led to the alumina smelter to be established by Comalco at Bluff, the city's port.

While these differences in rates of increase, size and growth of population among the regional cities can largely be accounted for by the productivity of their hinterlands, it is also necessary to recognize that differences in accessibility to their respective metropolitan centres have been significant factors in stimulating or retarding their growth. Wellington is probably the best example of the effect of difficult access in stimulating increased growth in its satellites. Shut in by hills and mountain ranges, separated from part of its hinterland by the stormy gap of Cook Strait, access to the capital has never been easy. As a result, Palmerston North, Wanganui and Nelson have probably grown somewhat larger than they would have done had Wellington been more accessible. By way of contrast, the relative ease of access to Christchurch from most parts of the Canterbury plains contributes to its dominating position and the fact that only one regional city has developed within its sphere of influence. The near-flat site of Christchurch and, in the case of Wellington, the gross shortage of easy land on which to expand have also affected their growth and discouraged or encouraged the development of regional cities within their respective hinterlands.

All four major cities have developed port facilities around the naturally sheltered harbour sites which were selected for initial settlement. Nine of the thirteen regional cities are also ports of varying size and significance. Difficulties of land communications through the tangled bush clothing the broken country and, for a time, a hostile Maori population encouraged the selection of coastal sites for early settlement. Dependence on the sea for communications gave those towns established on the coast an initial advantage as growing points. The four cities which today are significant regional foci and which are not on the coast each have certain specific site and situational attributes which have contributed to their ability to compete with the other port cities. Hamilton is sited on the banks of the Waikato river which was used for transporting goods and passengers until a rail connection was established with Auckland in 1874. Rotorua, distant from coast and port, was linked to Tauranga by coach and later to Auckland by rail in order to provide access to its tourist and spa facilities. Palmerston North is situated at the mouth of the Manawatu gorge which provides one of the few gaps in the mountain axis between East Cape and Cape Palliser. Hastings, though inland, has an effective port outlet through its twin city, Napier, only ten miles to the north. The two cities have virtually merged as the fringe of one is almost the beginning of the other.

The metropolitan centres

Auckland is by far the largest of New Zealand's cities, and the growth prospects of both its urban-based activities and its rich and dynamic hinterland provide assurance of its continuing urban primacy. Planners assume that the urban area will attain a population of 1 million in little more than a decade, though by world standards even this figure now represents a relatively small city.

The dominant characteristic of all New Zealand cities, and of Auckland in particular, is the vast space they consume in housing their residents. New Zealanders have for long demanded and secured the detached family dwelling on the quarter-acre section as the ideal and standard form of housing. Increasingly today, cheaper forms of subdivision offer sections of one-fifth of an acre; and the beginnings of a preference for flats is helping to increase, if only slightly, the very low residential densities. But despite these relatively minor changes in form and character, the cities continue to sprawl over extensive areas.

The Auckland urban area stretches almost forty miles from north to south and, in places, twenty-five miles from east to west. The total built-up area is approximately 140 square miles. This makes it a very large city in areal extent if not in the numbers of its people. The wastefully and extravagantly expansive nature of the urban area is partly attributable to the city's site, although much more to social demands and aspirations. The bulk of the city is spread over a narrow, sinuous isthmus which separates the Pacific Ocean from the Tasman Sea. The interpenetration of land and sea is marked, and in two places only about half a mile separates the Manukau and Waitemata harbours. The two harbours provide the city with access to both the east and west coasts of the North Island, although the bar-blocked mouth of the Manukau and its shallow waters restrict the use of the port of Onehunga to coastal vessels.

Dotted over the isthmus and on areas peripheral to it are a rash of small volcanic cones which provide excellent vantage points. Many of these cones were utilized by the Maori in pre-European times as *pa* sites, and an intricate system

31. *Auckland*

Much of Auckland sprawls over the isthmus between the Waitemata Harbour on the Pacific (foreground) and the Manukau Harbour, Tasman Sea (in the distance). The wharves and CBD are to the right of the photo. Behind the camera and tied to the CBD by the Auckland Harbour Bridge (just off the photo to the right) is the North Shore with a residential population approaching 100,000.

of terracing and pallisading rendered them veritable fortresses in time of inter-tribal warfare. The terracing is still clearly observable on cones such as Mount Eden (Maungawhau), One Tree Hill (Maungakiekie), and Mangere. Few of the cones now remain in their original state as the red scoria and blue basalt have been quarried and crushed for road metal and other industrial uses. Most cones have almost literally been levelled and entirely removed by human agency. A few have been preserved by virtue of the fact that they were early proclaimed public parks and domains. Today sheep are grazed within the built-up area on crisp short pastures on the steep slopes of such cones. Others again are capped by concrete water reservoirs or their craters sealed as water storage containers for nearby suburbs, while on several restaurants and kiosks enjoy delightful views of the city and its harbours. A summer nylon-tracked ski slope is planned for the steep southerly quarry-scarred slopes of Mount Wellington.

The lower easier slopes on the flanks of the remaining cones and a series of parallel ridges terminating in cliffed-promontories on both harbours have strongly influenced the pattern of Auckland's residential growth. The most prestigeous and valuable residential building sites are those which are elevated and offer either sea views or beach access. The expansion of settlement has followed the ridges, sought out the choice sites on the sunny and sheltered northern slopes of cones, cliff sites along the coast or lots along beach frontages. Exposed southerly slopes and valleys have been left to be infilled by less costly homes at a later stage when demand and waste travelling time and distance make them more attractive. The alternation of ridge and valley with the characteristic association of high income homes on the heights and smaller houses of more modest cost and design in the valleys is repeated throughout the isthmus in suburbs both old and new. The process is being duplicated in the newest areas of residential expansion to the north, south, east and west of the isthmus where ribbons of new dwellings follow the ridge tops and the valleys are left in scrub and gorse and farmland to be absorbed at a later stage.

To the west of the city the andesitic Waitakere ranges reach a height of 1,500 feet and form a bulwark against which the prevailing and boisterous westerly winds expend some of their energy and precipitation. The partly forested area forms one of the two catchments for the city's water supply. Exploited for their kauri timber at the end of the nineteenth century, the Waitakeres are now covered with a dense growth of secondary bush and scrub which provide scenic walks and drives for the city's half million people. The greywacke Hunua range to the southeast is another bush-covered catchment area close to the city. To the east, an inner and outer group of islands in the Hauraki gulf afford the Waitemata harbour a sheltered aspect in all but times of northeasterly gales. The two harbours, the gulf, the offshore islands, the bush-covered Waitakeres and Hunuas, the public parks on the cratered cones, and the miles of beaches along the indented coastline provide a wide range of recreational activities and scenic attractions within and around the city.

Following its choice as the site for the capital of the new colony by Governor Hobson in 1840, Auckland soon lost its hegemony to the more rapidly developing southern sectors of the country. The development of the South Island economy on the basis of gold, grain and golden fleece attracted the bulk of the pioneer population, and in 1865 the capital was moved to a more central location at Wellington. It was not until the conclusion of the Maori Wars and the development of refrigeration that the North Island began to overtake its southern counterpart. Since then the North Island has forged steadily ahead and Auckland has claimed and enjoyed more than its equal share of this growth.

The growth of Auckland can be attributed not only to its prosperous agricultural hinterland – over two-fifths of the total population live within the area served by Auckland – but also to its role as a major port and employment centre accumulating and distributing raw materials and processed goods. The utilization of the Waikato river for hydroelectric power, geothermal steam at Wairakei for further power production, the coal deposits at Huntly and Maramarua for domestic and industrial fuel and for electricity generation, the postwar boom in forestry activities in the central North Island – resulting in the establishment of special towns such as Tokoroa, Kawerau and Murupara – the cement, glass works and oil refinery at Whangarei, have all made a substantial contribution both directly and indirectly to Auckland's growth.

Auckland itself is also the largest manufacturing centre in New Zealand and accounts for more than 30 per cent of the total value of the national manufacturing output. A large proportion of the new postwar industries of New Zealand have been established in Auckland. Most of these industries have been designed to replace and substitute for imports as a means of saving foreign exchange and to create local employment. Such industries tend to be concerned with assembly or fabrication of components from semifinished materials. The first new industries to be developed were in the manufacture of clothing, footwear and foodstuffs but to these have been added a full range of industries producing consumer durables – motor vehicles, domestic appliances, radio and TV equipment. The opening of a steel rolling mill near the head of the Mangere inlet in 1962 and the construction of a steel works at Waiuku, forty miles southwest of the city, marks the beginning of a new phase of industrial growth.

Whereas most of the industrial establishments, apart from noxious factories such as freezing works, were previously located in the inner city, today there is a thin, discontinuous collar of industrial activities on the periphery of the isthmus stretching from Panmure-Mount Wellington in the southeast, through Penrose-Otahuhu-Onehunga in the south, to Mount Roskill and on to New Lynn and Rosebank Road in the west and northwest. These comprise a wide variety of activities and structures ranging from the smoke and grime and age of long-established brick, tile and pottery works at New Lynn to the green lawns and landscaped properties of modern chemical and paper products units along Rosebank Road; to sawmills and timber yards, glass works and vehicle assembly and furniture manufactures in the Penrose-Otahuhu area; to paint factories, motor mower and refrigerator assembly plants in modern, long, low buildings at Mount Wellington; to a miscellany of activities housed in sheds built by American troops during the second world war to store their equipment and supplies. Further south, almost on the present fringe of the city at Wiri, plans are being laid to develop a large area for industry to provide local outer suburban employment and so to reduce traffic flows to the central city.

The freezing works with their associated stockyards, holding paddocks, rail sidings and noxious fertilizer works are essential and peculiar features of the New Zealand urban scene. They consume a vast acreage of land in the Otahuhu area of Auckland where they are closely integrated establishments for the slaughter, freezing and dispatch of farm livestock to the local and export markets, and for the processing of a multitude of by-products in tanneries, boiling down works, wool scouring, and fellmongery units. They are very large, unsightly and smelly factories which are kept especially busy in the spring and early summer as the fat stock comes forward from the farms. The area is an unkempt and unappealing jumble of activity, studded with rocky basalt outcrops, rough wasteland, piles of phosphate and bright yellow sulphur, workers' cars parked on untidy stretches of rubbish-littered land reclaimed from the Manukau where formerly the industrial wastes were discharged to pollute the harbour and its surrounds with nauseous fumes. Heavily grazed, at times almost grassless holding paddocks, dusty stockyards filled with animals being sorted and channelled into pens by yapping dogs and shouting men rattling tin lids on wire loops, trucks unloading stock from farms, trainloads of sheep and cattle wagons bringing beasts for slaughter, and faded-white refrigerated vans to convey the frozen carcasses to the port, plumes of steam, noise and bustle, all are signs of the close and essential relationships which exist between the rural and urban economy in New Zealand.

Much of Auckland's national economic dominance stems from its position as a major focus for overseas transport services. The overseas port on the Waitemata comprises a series of short wharves built out into the harbour from the reclaimed shore of the commercial area and served by rail from the nearby central railway station. Largest and most significant units on the waterfront are the great refrigerated stores which hold dairy produce awaiting export. Enclosed conveyor systems carry the butter and cheese across busy city streets direct from the stores to the holds of vessels while refrigerated rail vans deliver frozen carcasses to the ships' sides where they are slung aboard by one of the ranks of gantry cranes. On the eastern and western ends of the port are the large silver-painted oil storage tanks. Further reclamation is now making provision for sufficient space to cope adequately with future container traffic, while a roll-on roll-off berth has been established for inter-island trade.

Air transport has been largely of postwar development and both internal and external services have grown at high annual rates. On its completion in 1965 the new Auckland International Airport at Mangere, which was built out across the mudflats of the Manukau harbour, linked Auckland and New Zealand with the main trans-Pacific jet airliner services.

Traffic circulation within the city is being improved by the continuing construction of an extensive motorway system of which thirty-five miles had been completed in 1968. On the one hand, the four- to six-laned system is probing both north and south through built-up area and farmland to give rapid access to farflung suburbs and to the hinterland. On the other hand, a complex system of interchanges, tunnels, underpasses, flyovers and viaducts in the central city is being developed – often utilizing the valleys and bulldozing clearings and swathes through old dilapidated dwellings in Grafton and Newton – to give freer and quicker access to the commercial areas, the port and railway marshalling yards, wholesale and bulk storage sheds. Both sections of the system, that through the suburbs to the periphery and that in the central city, will eventually be linked via the harbour bridge spanning the Waitemata to provide a rapid combination of routes through and within the city. The four-laned harbour bridge, which was completed in 1959, has already been found inadequate for the traffic volumes using it and by 1969 had been widened by the addition of two extra lanes on either side of the existing structure.

The central core of the city is focused on Queen Street in the Ligar valley, and a series of subsidiary streets parallel to it which run south from the Waitemata waterfront. Active growth and change are in evidence through the demolition of old buildings, and the erection of numerous office and hotel structures many of which have more than ten storeys. Until the late 1950s, the urban profile was low and squat and tucked away in the gully but today the vertical development of office, administrative, hotel and university buildings is giving the central city a much more lively and interesting appearance. Arms of the motorway system and interchanges to the east, west and south of the commercial core, the waterfront to the north, and sacrosanct splashes of green such as the Domain and Albert and Victoria parks will restrict future lateral development and place further emphasis on vertical growth in the centre of the city. While major industrial units have been located or relocated on the periphery of the isthmus, or even more distant from the centre, the fringe areas of the commercial core still retain a varied assortment of smaller factories interspersed among retail, wholesale and old residential structures. In addition, a number of larger industrial uses such as the gasworks, oil storage, flour milling and railway marshalling yards are still in the inner city area.

In all cities, the suburbs comprise the greater part of the urban landscape. The extent of suburban sprawl is heightened in Auckland, as in other cities in the country, by the New Zealander's long-term addiction to the 'cult of the quarter-acre section', or house lot. Suburbia is characterized by an endless sea of red corrugated iron-roofed, weather-boarded detached villas and bungalows, with brick and tile becoming increasingly popular as building materials in the more recently established areas. There is a strong emphasis on neatly manicured sections with lawns, gardens, paths, garages and houses set out in a rather regimented fashion. Trees and shrubs, both native and introduced, deciduous and evergreen, tropical palms and bananas and exotic flowering species enhance the view and brighten the scene with a spectrum of greenery. In all suburbs there is a considerable mixture of architectural styles. This mixture results from site characteristics and the evolution of transport in the city. Ridges and promontories were claimed first. Suburban horse, and later electric tram routes followed the ridges so that each tram stop occasioned a small nodule of housing built in the style of the period in which the track reached that particular point. The bus and car brought about infilling at distances from the tram routes and in the gullies and less desirable areas at a later stage so that a mixture of old and new housing is generally found within a short distance. The suburban rail link to the western and southern suburbs had a similar effect while the introduction of urban motorways is now bringing about a realignment of suburban patterns in response to the faster commuting offered by the private car. This history of development has meant that it is almost impossible to find in Auckland, or any other New Zealand city, street after street with exactly the same type of dwelling or even an individual suburb where styles have been regimented to the whims of a particular style in vogue.

Those suburbs which were initially developed before the end of the second world war show the greatest variation in housing styles. These were the areas most affected by changing circumstances in transport and income so that the mixture of house types, ages and quality is greatest. Such suburbs range from the 'established' high income areas of Remuera and Epsom with their mature stands of deciduous and evergreen trees, solid, frequently two-storeyed homes, and large – sometimes one- or two-acre – sections, to the middle-class suburbs of Point Chevalier and Mount Eden where, in the case of the former, small 'baches' of a once popular beach resort are now incorporated in a sea of wooden bungalows and tiled Spanish-Californian stucco dwellings. A quite distinctive group of suburbs are those fronting the Tamaki Drive to the east of the city where a series of beaches and the Tamaki Estuary emphasize the 'marine' nature of these communities – yacht clubs with hulls on cradles, moorings in protected bays displaying a wide range of craft from slim, graceful keelers and elaborate launches to modest inboard and outboard runabouts. Suburbs such as Mission Bay, Kohimarama, St Heliers and Glendowie earn their reputation as 'desirable' residential areas from this intimate relationship with the sparkling Waitemata where on occasions in summer the water is speckled with thousands of sails.

In contrast with the older mixed suburbs, there are two types of residential areas where uniformity of style is most apparent. Those areas developed by the state – primarily in the years immediately after the second world war when housing in general was in short supply – and the more recent subdivisions of building companies specializing in standardized, mass produced, modest homes on low cost sections – the 'group houses' in New Zealand terminology. Between 1936 and 1950, some 12,000 state houses were built in Auckland. In fact, one half of all the residential building in the Auckland area between 1936 and 1954 was carried out by the state. In West Tamaki some 3,000 state dwelling units were erected between 1945 and 1948. In addition, more than 1,000 sections were made available by the Crown to persons who wished to build their own houses in the area. Mount Roskill, another state housing area, had 1,200 houses erected after the war. In all, by 1964, 18,808 state rental house units had been built. At that time there were an estimated 140,000 dwellings in Auckland of which state houses comprised more than 13 per cent of the total.

The group housing areas are, in fact, more varied in individual house styles than the state house areas but generally have the common denominator of low-priced sections and fall into the lower price range for home purchase. Although efforts are made to vary the dwellings in any one area as it is developed, the limited range in price reduces variation to a marked degree. The standardized model, allowing for differences in shape, is the three-bedroomed bungalow of about 900 to 1,100 square feet set on one-fifth of an acre section, clad in weather-boards and with a tiled or corrugated iron roof.

In both state and group housing areas – the two are often combined in major development areas today as the state offers more opportunity for private enter-prise – some attention has been given to planning the street system so that they differ from the rectangular pattern of older suburbs. Cul-de-sacs, crescents and curvilinear streets are common, although not now restricted to these two forms of housing area. Increasingly in all new subdivisions attempts are being made to provide underground electric power and telephone connections so that the web of power lines and the forest of leaning hardwood poles characteristic of older suburbs are often absent in newer housing areas.

During the last decade a change in attitude to the type of acceptable home has occurred; and, in many of the older suburbs on the isthmus, new flats and home units have been appearing and old houses converted to flats. At this stage of the city's development they are simple in form, generally single-storeyed and con-taining, perhaps, three or four units. This has done little to raise the low resi-dential densities in the suburbs but is possibly an encouraging sign for the future. Ten years ago people were convinced that New Zealanders would not live in flats but today the growing popularity of this form of residence may be an incipient sign, if not yet a firm assurance, that the endless sprawl accompany-ing the growth of the country's cities may be checked. At the other extreme, and very isolated in their occurrence as yet, has been the development of several tower blocks of luxury home units. These cater for persons in the upper income bracket and are not likely to occur on a wide scale.

In response to the suburban shift in population, several large shopping centres designed on the mall principle have been built in the outlying suburbs at Pakuranga, New Lynn and Manurewa. Areas of parking are set aside to accom-modate the private car and a wide range of retail goods is available. A number of the leading retail stores in the central business district have established branch outlets in such centres to offset the relative decline in retail patronage in the central city.

The consumption of space by low density residential development has had a further effect on the fringes of New Zealand cities – an effect which has its parallels overseas. Intensive agricultural activities such as town milk supply, market gardening, orcharding and viticulture have been continually subjected to the pressure of demand for land from urban housing to shift away from the city fringe. Open grassy green acres of rich volcanic soil in many parts of Auckland, as at Mangere, Rosebank, Te Atatu and Henderson, have been abandoned in favour of housing and industry; and dairying, gardening and orcharding have all been forced to locate at increasingly greater distances from the city. On the other hand, the immediate presence of a large market and the ability to capitalize on this by providing roadside sales has meant that many smallholders producing fresh fruits and vegetables have been able to resist for a while economic pressures to sell their land. In season, the heavy weekend traffic of Aucklanders seeking bulk quantities of fresh produce such as apples, pears, peaches, strawberries and vegetables at roadside stalls and wine from local vineyards is clear evidence of the ability of such intensive agricultural forms to compete temporarily with sprawl. In addition, proximity to suburban areas has meant a ready supply of married women and teenagers for casual labour. As a result, there are numerous small pockets of intensive agricultural production which are now almost completely surrounded by housing and which, for a limited period at least, continue to resist the encroachment of urban uses.

In common with most other western cities, Auckland has an inner ring of older residences fringing the CBD which are slowly being replaced. This inner area can hardly be called a slum by overseas standards although there is or has been evidence of dilapidation, lack of public utilities, overcrowding and relatively high residential densities. A mixture of old, large dwellings and small, workers' cottages have been converted to flats and rooming houses. The combined efforts of the state and the city council in demolishing these old, sub-standard dwellings and replacing them with blocks of flats, pensioner flats and town houses is currently under way. Demolition is not always followed by residential replacement. Many of the dwellings in Grafton and Newton stood in the way of urban motorways and large areas of inner city housing have been cleared for the routeways and interchanges of modern highway development. Along the main radial routes leading from the CBD – the Great South Road, New North Road and Great North Road – another form of either conversion or replacement has taken place with the development of ribbons of commercial use displacing former residential units.

The occupants of the residences in the inner areas have been the most recent non-European migrants to the city – the Maori in the immediate postwar years and, largely within the last decade, the Pacific Islander. The Maori population of Auckland totals more than 40,000 and the Pacific Islanders more than 16,000 – in all, almost one-tenth of the total population is 'Polynesian'. In parts of the inner area the non-European component comprises over 35 per cent of the total population. However, although this trend of new non-European migrants settling in the central city appears to be sustained there is evidence that with peripheral state housing, dwellings erected specifically for Maoris by the Department of Maori Affairs and group housing, many of the non-European people formerly occupying inner city locations are now moving to new suburbs on the fringe of the city. This redistribution has been quite spectacular. In 1956, for example, the administrative area of Auckland City proper housed 50 per cent of all the urban area's Maoris. By 1966, this figure had declined to 25 per cent and Manukau City, the southernmost sector of the urban area, housed 30 per cent of the total Maori population compared with 9 per cent only ten years earlier. This is a trend quite different from that experienced in most western cities and is largely the result of the absence of an active policy of segregation in the country as a whole combined with the availability to wage-earners of low-interest finance for home building and purchase through the State Advances Corporation.

Auckland is a bright city with its predominantly gaily-painted wooden houses displaying a technicolour scene ranging from the more conservative creams and whites of the older areas with their red or green corrugated iron roofs, through the whole spectrum of pastel shades of exterior paint and multicoloured tiles in the newer housing areas. Almost all the houses have a garage or carport for the family car, or cars, and in many suburbs the streets are lined with additional vehicles – frequently of dubious age – which represent the family's second car or one belonging to a teenager in the household. The residential areas are liberally endowed with green patches of sports grounds, parks and race-courses.

Auckland, then, is the largest of the New Zealand metropolitan centres but illustrates many characteristics common to its three southern counterparts. Universities, technical institutes, private primary and secondary schools, major sections of government departments, medical specialists and specialized hospital units, transport facilities and difficulties, clearly defined industrial areas and loosely woven, low density residential areas distinguishable in terms of quality, age and, to a lesser extent, social class are all common to the four metropolitan centres of New Zealand.

Variations in site characteristics and attributes are largely responsible for the differences in the form of the other three cities. Cut off from the rest of the North Island by the southern tail of the Tararua range, Wellington faces south into the frequently wild, bleak and windswept narrow expanse of Cook Strait. The harbour, Port Nicholson, is guarded by Barretts Reef, a permanent danger to shipping. Flat land in the city itself is limited, and most of that has been reclaimed and taken up by commercial and transport facilities. Residential areas have tucked themselves into small bays around the harbour, scrambled over the steep gorse and light bush-covered hills to dig out and excavate small terraces on which to site houses, or followed the foot of the fault scarp northeastwards along the harbour to the deltaic alluvial flatland of the Hutt valley where industry and housing have found living space and the only extensive area of easy alluvial ground for development. Northwards over the hills towards the sand dunes and west coast beaches, a chain of smaller centres from Johnsonville, Tawa, Porirua, Titahi Bay, Plimmerton and Paekakariki have grown up along the electrified rail link to supply commuter dormitories for the city.

Apart from its difficult and distinctive site, Wellington is best known for the role it plays as the capital of the country. The concentration of old wooden and new plate glass office buildings housing the various government departments, Parliament House itself, the head offices of financial and commercial enterprises for the whole country, emphasise its importance as the seat of power and the the centre of decision-making.

The city's site has imposed major difficulties on its transport system. A narrow strip of flat land perched between the sea and the foot of the fault scarp connects the city by road and electrified commuter rail services to the Hutt valley. The road and rail routes to the north and to the Hutt converge at the base of the hills and at the head of the harbour. Congestion at this point is at its peak and space for easing the problem at a premium. A motorway system to relieve some of the pressure is currently under construction but even this has had to step out over reclaimed land on piles and over a web of rail lines to gain space. The airport at Rongotai had to be partly reclaimed from the sea and is bordered to the east and west by steep hills. The cable-car from the commercial core rises steeply to the Kelburn heights and is another reflection of the difficulties of communications imposed by the site.

Wellington, too, has its state housing areas at Porirua and in the Hutt valley, older inner residential areas undergoing renewal, and miscellaneous assortment of nondescript suburbs. Of all the cities, Wellington has developed higher residential densities with more emphasis on blocks of flats. This has been partly to maximize the use of a restricted site and partly in response to the demand by civil servants, politicians, diplomats, and personnel in private enterprise who are continually moving in and out of the city.

But the suburban streets winding around the hills and the homes perched on their little manmade terraces reached by hundreds of steps and stairs, are characteristic. The views from elevated house sites and hilltop vantage points are often quite spectacular. On a fine day Wellington can be a very attractive city. On a cold winter day with strong gusty winds funnelled through Cook Strait and eddying into Port Nicholson, and with snow lying along the tops of the Tararuas, it can be miserable.

Christchurch is different from Auckland and Wellington in terms of both its site and form. It is considered by some sentimentally imaginative but ill-informed New Zealanders to be the most 'English' of the cities. Set largely on the coastal boundary of the Canterbury plains, the city has a formalized rectangular – and totally un-English – street pattern scarcely affected by the Avon and Heathcote rivers which meander through the built-up area. The focus of the city is the 'square', centre piece of which is the pinnacle steeple of the Anglican cathedral. To the south, the outer rim of a breached volcanic crater forms the Port hills. The inner section of the crater now almost encloses the sheltered waters of Lyttleton harbour. The port is connected to the city by road and rail tunnels. Further south, on Banks Peninsula, the little settlement of Akaroa huddles near the water in another breach of the volcanic mass and now shows little indication of the original French influence in its founding. To the east of the city, suburban development along the dune coast at New Brighton has created a linear marine suburb. Far to the west, on a clear day, can be seen the snow-mantled rampart of the Southern Alps and to the north the peaks of the Seaward Kaikouras.

The grassy banks of the willow-lined Avon with its rowing boats and native ducks, the wide expanse of Hagley Park sprinkled with golden daffodils in spring and framed by the stone buildings of the old university, the museum, the hospital, teachers' college and Christ's College (where the boys still wear boaters) – these plus the cathedral and the legacy of the Canterbury squatto-cracy in the hinterland have contributed to the city's distinctiveness.

In contrast to the 'English' character of Christchurch, Dunedin is recognized as the 'Scottish' centre of New Zealand. Set at the southwestern end of the long narrow slit which forms the Otago harbour, the city has grown in a semicircle stretching from the coast in the south across the narrow base of the peninsula and follows the line of the harbour in a northeasterly direction. Centre of the city is the Octagon with the nearby dark grey stone of Knox's Presbyterian church, a statue of Robert Burns, and the town hall dominant. The prevalence of old grey, grimy stone buildings in the commercial core, the obvious lack of new office buildings, a population which is barely increasing and, by New Zealand standards, a somewhat rigorous climate, make Dunedin the least attractive of the metropolitan centres.

A century ago, the city was the dominant urban area in the country when Dunedin's hinterland was inundated with diggers in search of gold. At that time numerous firms which developed national markets were established there and a number of the plants and head offices of New Zealand-wide firms still remain. The woollen mills both within the city and a few miles to the west on the Mosgiel plain are examples of long-established and national industries. The first of New Zealand's universities was established in Dunedin and the medical school, in particular, has a long and illustrious reputation.

However, the city can scarcely be considered as a point of dynamic urban growth. The population of the Dunedin urban area has increased by only 19,872 people in the period 1926 to 1966 while Auckland, Wellington-Hutt and Christchurch have all more than doubled their population in the same time.

Indeed, with the rapid growth of several regional cities, especially Hamilton and Invercargill, it is unlikely that Dunedin will remain the fourth largest urban area in the country by the turn of the century.

The regional cities

Apart from the four metropolitan centres and some constituent administrative units within them, the thirteen regional cities are the only urban areas which possess city status. In effect, the regional cities began, and continue to function, as part of the service town network. Their origins are similar to those of the country towns and they are really only overgrown rural service centres except that, in the process of growing up, they have added functions which enable them to offer a wider and more complete range of services over a larger area than the country towns.

The advantages which made possible the development of regional cities stemmed largely from their centrality and accessibility. Their coastal location and port function have already been noted. From the time of their establishment the future regional cities operated as focal points for the accumulation and distribution of new settlers, imported machinery, implements and materials and as outlets for the export of timber, gold, grain, wool, butter, cheese and lamb from their hinterlands. As the pioneers pushed further inland other towns were established to provide for the new farming communities and each regional centre developed a swarm of country towns within its orbit.

Those cities which were based on ports have experienced changes in their relative importance as shipping and roads and railways and air services have been improved. In the case of Whangarei and Tauranga, the ports have taken on very specialized roles for the country as a whole in addition to maintaining their tasks as general cargo handlers. New Zealand's only oil refinery is set within the deep sheltered entrance of the Whangarei harbour and a regular procession of tankers, arriving with crude oil from Sabah and the Middle East, and smaller local tankers distributing the refined products to coastal ports and storage and distribution points for consumption throughout the country, has spectacularly raised the tonnage of cargo handled. Tauranga's main support as a leading port derives from the timber and timber products of the central North Island. Logs, sawn timber, pulp and paper are all railed or roaded to the port for dispatch primarily to Japan and Australia. The increased shipping, which has resulted, stimulated the extension and improvement of facilities at Mount Maunganui. Gisborne has become a fishing port to supply the local food freezing plant established there as well as drawing on the intensive cropping of the Poverty Bay flats for corn, peas and fruit and other produce for canning and freezing. Logs from its hinterland and meat from its freezing works also keep it busy. New Plymouth, Timaru and Napier also function as outlets for wool and for the produce from freezing works in either the cities proper or in their hinterland. Napier has had to build an artificial breakwater and dredge its port area following the earthquake in 1931, which raised the bed of the original harbour so drastically that large vessels could no longer use it.

The regional cities are now closely linked to the major communication networks of the country by state highways and rail services. In addition, the National Airways Corporation operates frequent daily services to the regional cities which connect them with each other and with the metropolitan centres. They all have their own radio stations and daily newspapers which maintain close relationships between the cities and their service areas.

In both Hamilton and Palmerston North, a university and teachers' training college have been established in the last decade. Massey University of the Manawatu at Palmerston North was founded on the basis of an agricultural college which had operated for almost half a century. All the regional cities differ from the country towns in that they have single sex high schools – as distinct from coeducational colleges – for both boys and girls. Whereas the country town has its Roman Catholic primary school, the cities have private schools of several denominations and these often provide education at the secondary level. Technical colleges may also be present in the regional cities.

All the cities are major administrative centres with a supreme court, regional offices of government departments such as Lands and Survey, Labour and Employment, Social Security, Forestry, Agriculture, Works, and within northern cities, Maori Affairs. Some now have regional planning authorities. The administrative role of the cities is further emphasized by the fact that the newest and often the largest buildings in the cities are either those of insurance companies and banks or the headquarters of a group of government departments. Base hospitals both to serve the city's population and to supplement the small maternity hospitals in the country towns, as well as private hospitals are further indications of the higher status and development of the regional cities.

While all have retained the basic ribbon development of a single commercial street which characterizes the country towns, the regional cities have developed in some depth from their initial main street and in the height of new buildings in the business core. The low profile of the commercial area is pierced with several-storeyed office and administrative buildings added in recent years. Whangarei has expanded around the triangular streets close to the original town wharf; Tauranga along its waterfront; Hamilton around its 'Garden Place'; Palmerston North about its square; Invercargill eastwards from the Waihopai river; Timaru from its harbour base on Caroline Bay; Rotorua from its early focus on the railway station; and Napier from its marine parade. Within the retail section a greater range of department stores and the addition of speciality establishments provide a more comprehensive selection of goods than can the smaller country towns. Wholesale organizations act as outlets for the supply of goods both to the city retailers and to those in the country towns within their respective spheres of influence. Heavy and specialized farm machinery showrooms and yards are characteristic.

In almost all cases the regional cities have either within their administrative areas or adjacent to them certain specialized establishments or activities which have supplemented their service centre role and which operate on a broader level than merely to serve their own particular region. The cement and glass works and the oil refinery at Whangarei; the Ruakura agricultural research station and the airforce camp at Te Rapa close to Hamilton; the military camps at Linton and Ohakea and the former agricultural college at Massey, in the case of Palmerston North; the Cawthron Institute for biological and agricultural research near Nelson; the proposed alumina smelter at Bluff, Invercargill's port; viticulture in the vicinity of Hastings; food freezing in Gisborne; the national and international attractions of Rotorua's thermal activity; agricultural chemicals at New Plymouth; these are all activities which provide goods, services or facilities to a major portion of New Zealand if not the entire national market.

Apart from a wide range of agricultural servicing industry, geared to the demands of the farming hinterland, industrial growth in the regional cities is largely confined to a more restricted combination of protected and import replacement industries similar in kind, though perhaps smaller in size, to those found in the metropolitan centres.

Freezing works are the most common processing factories in the cities. Closely allied to the freezing works, are the large saleyards where stock from a wide area is accumulated on sale day. Specialist and essential farm services such as aerial topdressing, well boring, road works, building and construction, hauliers, soil testing and catchment consultants are available in the regional cities.

The stud ram, bull and horse sales held in the cities draw a clientele from all over the country and even wealthy American or Australian buyers or representatives from the World Bank or FAO looking for first class racing or breeding animals. So, too, the agricultural and pastoral shows held either once or twice a year in each of the cities are major regional events at which farm equipment and livestock are the centre pieces of the week-long activities.

In the largely industrialized contemporary nations with specialization of production and nationwide – if not worldwide – markets, the concept and reality of the city-region has lost much of its regional meaning. In the New Zealand context, however, the city is closely tied to the rural activities and productivity of its hinterland. The two are intimately linked in an interchange of goods and services. While the cities have acquired a thin veneer of urban sophistication which is absent in the smaller country towns, the covering is indeed thin and the influence of the rural environment in which they are set seldom far below the surface.

Part Five
The changing aspect

Chapter 11
The future pattern of the landscape

Careful long-term planning of land use, landscape and quality of life in New Zealand is still alien in thought and unusual in practice. For it is a country still pervaded by pioneering attitudes of mind. It is inclined to the practical approach which it prefers to the deliberately studious and theoretical. It still favours trial and error, even to do or die, in preference to calculated and scientifically based planning and preparation.

It was therefore an unusually enlightened and unaccustomed step that was taken by the New Zealand Institute of Engineers when in November 1967 it promoted and organized in Auckland – of all places – 'The New Zealand Countryside in 1980' Conference. Its aim and object in calling together representatives of the many and varied interests involved was to ensure that future changes in the countryside would 'reflect not only the best of technology but also a profound sense of what is truly valuable, and a deep care and respect for nature'.

There is of course much room for argument as to what *is* 'truly valuable' in the New Zealand countryside, or what is more 'truly valuable' than something else. There is no satisfactory, or widely used, or commonly accepted yardstick for measuring what features of the rural scene, or what amenities of the urban landscape, or what residual elements of the pre-European or pre-human environment are truly valuable and must therefore be declared of national interest and preserved and protected. It is most doubtful whether any measure of value likely to be suggested would even appeal to a majority of New Zealanders. New Zealand's is still in some ways a pioneer society, a community still not far from the colonial frontier, living pragmatically, close to the problems of the moment, and without deep sentimental attachments to the past. Its concern with the countryside is not with the antiquarian, the rustic, the 'history-impregnated', or the picturesque, but with the functional, with the land's active use and enjoyment, and with its future potential. The New Zealand landscape is not for gazing at and wonderment, but for doing things in either for profit or for pleasure. The countryside does not conjure up for New Zealanders the glories of an historic past, and rarely does it appeal to deep aesthetic emotions. The New Zealander's reaction to a scene that appeals to him is more likely to be expressed by some such phrase as 'That's a nice block of country for sheep', or 'What could you do with a thousand acres of land like that and the capital to develop it?' Devoid of a lengthy history and without deep-rooted traditions, still so largely concerned with taming a wilderness and moulding land to his requirements, the New Zealander's concern with historic monuments, with the residuals of a pre-European fauna and flora, with protection and preservation of what now exists, or remains over from a never distant past, is not a widespread, compulsive or popular involvement.

New Zealand society is young and dynamic. Its roots reach back to the British Isles rather than deeply into its native soils. Its values are not fixed, but change. They are often even fickle. What may be considered truly valuable by one generation may have little interest for another. For centuries the New Zealand bush was the Polynesian's principal resource and source of livelihood, but to the European it was a weed, a nuisance, an obstacle, a foe to be vanquished, something growing and occupying land where it was not wanted. And so the face of the North Island was rudely transformed. Few, if any, 'Kiwis' would now argue that the clearing of the forest and the swamps – in the Wairarapa, Manawatu, Taranaki, Waikato, Hauraki, Bay of Plenty and Southland – was not in the national interest, not a valuable, indeed epic and heroic, achievement. Contemplating the open sweep of the Canterbury plains and the tawny tussock foothills, the sharp angular outline of suites of river terraces and the jagged, 'precipitous, purple', snow-tipped skeleton of the Southern Alps, none would today condemn the moahunter who, in hunting and exterminating the moa almost a thousand years ago, probably removed a forest cover which once hemmed and restricted the view and smoothed the sharp outline of rock and scree and gully, and who made possible its replacement with a sea of bunched grasses tossed and rustled by the nor'wester. Which are New Zealanders – or visitors to their country – to assess as the more truly valuable: the productive hill country pastures of the North Island and the arable cropland of the South Island or the pervading forest that once clothed them in a visually dull and un-exciting but pristine grandeur?

What the antipodean rural landscape owes to nature and what to men is almost everywhere difficult to say. Even where man himself has rarely pene-trated – as, for example, in Fiordland – his influence is felt. Indirectly his disturbance is apparent. The pre-human biological order is disrupted by the animals, insects, plants, viruses and fungi he has imported and transmitted over the face of the land. The popular dichotomy of Man and Nature, the supposed antagonism between them, and the extremist view that things human are inevitably retrograde and things natural valuable and divine, are alike false and obstructive. Man has been present in New Zealand for little more than one fleeting millennium – present not only as an actor in a drama on a stage but also as a potent and imaginative stage designer who has constructed many features of the set as the plot proceeded. The contemporary countryside is the reflection of the ways in which a succession of people have appraised its qualities and resources in terms of their own capacity, skills and needs, and have used it to their own ends and filled it with works that expressed their way of life. A major distinction is that while in their isolation the Polynesians' capacity, skills and needs remained largely static, the Europeans' have been subject to continual, violent and erratic change. It is man who reveals the countryside's individuality by moulding it to his own purposes so that it becomes as Vidal de la Blache once said, a 'medal struck in the likenesses of the people' occupying it. It is more helpful, in contemplating the problems of the land, in prospecting the future aspect of the countryside, to think of man *in* nature, rather than man *and* nature as separable entities. What is needed is a 'deep care and respect', not so much for nature *per se* as for man in nature.

'The New Zealand Countryside in 1980' Conference wisely took a medium short-term look into the future of the country's urban and rural landscapes. The year 1980 was, at the end of 1967, but twelve brief and galloping years away. Viewed in the longer term perspective of even New Zealand's short European occupancy, the countryside will not change significantly in that time. Yet in terms of a human lifetime, in terms of the duration of the New Zealander's individual experience of the New Zealand scene, quite spectacular transformation is possible, indeed inevitable in twelve fleeting years. For confirmation of this he needs only to cast his mind back over the previous twelve years.

Since 1955 New Zealand has added 600,000 people to its population – more than in the first half-century of its European settlement, more than during half a century of hectic pioneering and of clearing bush and tussock. In the same period its non-European population has almost doubled. The electric energy at the New Zealander's command, has leaped from a daily average of 10 million kWh to 31 million. The state alone has brought almost a million acres of land into production and established in excess of 2,000 farm units. The livestock in the countryside have increased by more than 33 million ewe equivalents. The increase in motor vehicles in twelve years was in excess of the number using the highways in 1955 (652,000), more indeed than the increase in population. Twelve years ago New Zealand had no motorways, no jet airports, or jet air services. Internal air passenger traffic has meantime trebled and overseas traffic has increased sixfold. Twelve years ago the country had little more than half a million occupied dwellings – one to every 3·6 occupants. Since then almost a quarter of a million have been constructed; nearly one for every two persons added to the population. The number of baches and weekend cottages has doubled in twelve years. To appreciate the extent and mass of other forms of construction, one has only to push one's way through the pavement throng and beside the towering new office, insurance, bank and hotel buildings in Auckland's Queen Street, to wander round any of the seven university campuses, to ride in tight procession over the Auckland harbour bridge or to visit Kawerau, Wairakei or Benmore.

The twelve years to 1980 will see no lesser range or quantum of development, though the rate of expansion may diminish. Quantitative predictions based on statistical trends are available. It is more difficult to endeavour to convert cold statistical prognostications into a warm and living picture of what the rural countrysides and urban landscapes of 1980 might be like, and to depict what pleasure and problems they may present.

Prophecy is at present particularly difficult because of the economic situation in which the Dominion finds itself, with some surprise, after complacent years of prosperity and progress. It stands at crossroads of quite vital significance to the charting of its future countryside. External relations, as well as domestic politics and policies, will also have a place in planning and attainment. Such is the involved and cumulative effect of local and distant human decisions on the face of the land that General de Gaulle, or his successor, in preventing the United Kingdom's entry into the European Economic Community, may make more widespread and lasting impression on the New Zealand scene than the New Zealand Prime Minister and his Cabinet.

Nevertheless, one may boldly venture to predict that agriculture must remain the solid base of New Zealand's economy, of its superstructure of social services, of its living standards, and of its capacity to extend horizons and take advantage of constantly developing technology. But traditional patterns of land use and farm economy will change. If agricultural protectionism in Europe, North America and elsewhere prevents New Zealand from profitably disposing of its customary livestock products, the stimulus to change will strengthen and its pace accelerate. With improved techniques and new forms of management and organization, New Zealand pastoral agriculture will be capable of producing more and more from a declining acreage. Large-scale organization of capital to take maximum advantage of land and technology will mean larger farms, amalgamation of holdings and units running 1,000 dairy cows and 10,000 ewes where formerly half that number was run on a score of separate holdings. And livestock rearing could become more closely associated with cropping, with the growing of maize and barley, and associated in the landscape with structures necessary to store the crop. Indoor, stall or concrete pad feeding, especially of beef cattle and pigs, could become at long last a characteristic of the Dominion's livestock farming. Consequently, though carrying capacity may be stepped up and breeds may change, livestock need not be more conspicuously present in the landscape. With stable or diminishing annual overseas disposals of livestock products, much of the rougher, more difficult hill country and of the remote back country land will become surplus to farm requirements.

At the same time the best land, of easy contour and inherent fertility, or the more accessible land, artificially fertilized, will become the scene of operation of much more intensive uses – for arable agriculture, horticulture or orcharding. While inelasticity of demand for agricultural products relates principally to staple and standard products, it does not relate to the exotic luxury products, the new, strange taste and the out-of-season or expensive tidbit. The trickle of air-freighted exports from New Zealand of strawberries, asparagus spears, orchids, boysenberries, Chinese gooseberries, tamarillos, venison, smoked eel, crayfish, oysters, whitebait could become a flood. Already even the domestic market for citrus fruit and table grapes, for many sharply seasonal vegetables and for wines is far from satisfied. Orchards bigger than New Zealand has known before are already being established. Vineyards individually more expansive than the total area under the vine twenty years ago have been planted. Exchange-earning overseas markets have not yet been tried or tested.

Twelve short years may well be sufficient to reveal a retreat from the hilly unprofitable margins of pastoral farmland, providing more room for afforestation, recreation and conservation. At the same time, the Dominion may witness an intensified use of plains and downlands, the parts of the countryside New Zealanders see more frequently and are more aware of. These will be worked-in more thoroughly, occupied more densely, differentiated more sharply, and more warmly humanized, tamed and trimmed, gardened not grazed.

Yet, as has been the case since the land was first cleared and pioneered a century or more ago, there will remain what are untidy, underused, ill-treated or ignored stretches of hill country. New Zealand will not be rid of its weeds – gorse, blackberry, broom and boxthorn. Soil erosion will still be rife – robbing the nation of part of its inheritance. Indeed, the recent techniques and policies of more heavily stocking the land, of close grazing pastures, of carrying eight and ten ewes where until a decade ago three and four were considered to exert sufficient grazing pressure, have heightened the hazards of accelerated run-off and soil removal by surface wash and deep-seated slumping. Several high intensity – but not abnormally intensive – rains in the northern half of the North Island in the last three years have revealed this hazard, by bespattering hills with more ugly fresh yellow slump scars than have been apparent since aerial topdressing came to heal and clothe and grass over older wounds.

And the progress of the frontier of farm settlement, pushed into the pumice land of the Volcanic Plateau, the clay hills of Northland and the tawny tussock downland of Southland by the mechanical and technical forces organized and financed by the Land Development Division of the Department of Lands and Survey, has brought new dangers and novel forms of soil erosion. When proposals of the New Zealand Electricity Department and the Ministry of Works to raise the level of Lake Manapouri so that it is rimmed by stark black leafless stumps, or to cut highways through forested ridges leaving a canyon of ugly eroding batters, or of the Department of Lands to allow mining on unique, untouched island sanctuaries, create public disquiet and protest, it is an indication of the fact that New Zealand society is growing up. Whereas fifty – even twenty-five – years ago these would have gone unremarked, today a more conscientious and conversant public and press soon raise an outcry.

Both publicly and privately soil conservation is better, but far from adequately, organized. There are financial incentives and taxation savings for the farmer disturbed by soil erosion's drain on his land's productivity and for the landowner willing to plant his rough and scrub-covered rural investment in trees. The New Zealand Forest Service and the large private timber working concerns are again planting trees after a lapse of thirty years of apparent glut and oversupply. In 1968 a greater acreage was planted than at any time since the planting boom of the depression years in the 1930s. While the large scale planting may well continue to be overwhelmingly of *Pinus radiata* and Douglas fir, the breeding and distribution of vigorous, deep-rooted, fast-growing strains of poplars, willows and other deciduous and more decorous trees will add new hues and colours to farm and outer urban landscapes, especially since many farmers are regularly removing single, giant, weather-beaten specimens of macrocarpa and radiata as well as ancient pasture-occupying, ground-shading shelterbelts of conifers.

Whether the New Zealand economy faces increasing difficulty in selling its traditional primary products or not, whether the country considers as serious the threatened strengthening of the United Kingdom's ties with Europe or is convinced it will be accorded 'adequate safeguards', it would be wise in any event to launch a bold, venturesome and sufficient expansion of tourist facilities. For this it already has a remarkable and preeminently characteristic degree of scenic variety – indeed of oddity and uniqueness of countryside, both wild and cultivated. It has still land enough for both extensive and intensive agriculture, space enough to protect wildernesses, to provide access to mountain, snowfield, lake, river and surf-beaten shore, land for forests as well as fields, land for recreational use and enjoyment, for refuge, retreat and relief from the ills of urban confinement – not only for New Zealanders but for potential streams of more affluent, jet-speeded visitors from outside, from Japan and Russia as well as from Australia and North America. With preservation of the little modified, wild and remoter countryside, with careful cultivation and patient domestic care of the trim and tidy humanized landscapes, with conservation of soil and scenery, with better planned and culturally more exciting towns and cities, and with an audacious but judicious extension of tourist facilities, the flow of visitors could become an avalanche – itself adding to the diversity of scene and to the attraction of countrysides.

The nation's prosperity may well depend on such adaptations of land uses and countryside. But even though the rise in New Zealand living standards may be slowed or halted, population, possessions and paraphernalia will grow. The addition of 800,000 people to the population by 1980 may prove a little optimistic in view of the pill, tighter economic conditions and changing patterns of migration, but the Dominion will in any case have to accommodate an accretion of population greater than that of the last twelve years. He would be a bold man who was willing to predict that in the next decade or so mushrooming urbanization, the acquisition of motor vehicles and the development of soundly based industrial investment – in forestry, power production, tourism, transport, industries processing farm, forest and mineral products, etc. – will be less than in the decade from 1960 to 1970.

Although there will be fewer farmers, especially with capital intensification of agriculture and larger, more efficient – including joint stock company operated – units, there will certainly be many more people. Nine out of ten additions to the Dominion's population could live in cities and towns, especially in fast enlarged cities, and particularly on their rural perimeters. The swollen numbers of people will in future be more mobile than even in the recent past. The ratio of vehicles to population will continue to grow, facilities for travel will increase and the time taken by journeys will fall, even in some cases, with extension of urban motorways, in city centres. In the city much as in the country, there will be intensification of land use, activity and indeed of residence at or close to the centre, with a loose extravagant expansion of low density settlement at the increasingly distant perimeter. This farflung urban-rural fringe of scattered low-density settlement, scorned and resisted by planners and popular press as 'sprawl', will at least provide exciting opportunities for experiment and planning, nicely mixing intensive horticulture and extensive residential uses, reserves, open spaces and recreation facilities, appealingly varied afforestation, protected shorelines and, if necesssry, artificially created water bodies for multifarious recreational uses and enjoyment – all within an hour's run, say fifty miles, of daily congested, and nightly dull and depressing centres of urban pressures and neuroses.

In this expanded population the country can count on several other features. It will be increasingly New Zealand bred and born, reared and educated. It will be better informed and more aware of, and familiar with, the nation's countrysides and their lengthening history of modification, development and human moulding. It will be an older, more mature, technically better equipped population. It will be ethnically more diverse and culturally more distinctive. It will not be as overwhelmingly British and European in outlook. It will be 10 per cent Polynesian. In the North Island possibly 15 per cent of it will be made up of people with Maori or Pacific island blood. With the increasing clustering of human numbers in the northern half of the North Island, that is where the most impressive changes in life and landscape will be found. The dynamic humanizing of the countryside will be similarly concentrated in the country's northern reaches. By comparison, in twelve years South Island landscapes will, with local exceptions, appear to have remained stable and static.

Space does not provide here the opportunity of dealing with the many other facets of the New Zealand landscape's future, with the role of factory industry, of mining and quarrying, of fishing, of power development and transmission, of air and water pollution, of the eutrophication of lakes, of biological problems which in New Zealand are so often unique and scientifically fascinating. There is not room to discuss the philosophy, aims and attainments of planning; no opportunity to explore the peculiarities of New Zealand society which are reflected, incidentally, in urban and rural landscapes – race course, TAB's, beer drinking, the roadside litter of bottles, political attitudes and social conventions; no time to investigate vanishing volcanic scoria cones of the Auckland isthmus, the threat to Coppermine and other priceless island gems, or to estimate the place in the countryside of new power stations – atomic, thermal, geothermal and hydro-electric – or the part to be played by giant industrial complexes like the fast-arising iron and steel mill at Waiuku (south of Auckland) or the promised aluminium smelter at Bluff.

The future face of the land – like its present features – will be shaped and designed very largely by the daily toil, and ordinary endeavours of 3·5 million ordinary folk (in 1980) rather than by giant corporations or single large projects. The removing of its blemishes, the creating of new delights, and, inevitably, the careless or unintentional addition of new flaws, imperfections and ugly excrescences, will be in major part the outcome of the workaday activities of farmers, builders, contractors, and townsfolk, sometimes working individually, sometimes in groups and sometimes as a national community. Personal profit, or pleasure, and occasionally community benefit, will be the fuels that spark changes in the countryside. For the most part they will be individually small and insignificant. Cumulatively and together, and added to the more massive operations of state and local body agencies and those of powerful private corporations, changes in the countryside will mirror a symbiosis of land and life. The landscape of New Zealand in 1980, as in 980 and 1780, will represent the agency of man *in* nature, and be the product of habit and habitat irretrievably interwoven and mutually affecting each other.

The New Zealand scene will depend on the New Zealand society's attitudes and needs, on its culture, technology and institutions. These are for New Zealanders to frame. The New Zealand countryside of the future will be what New Zealanders want it to be and what New Zealanders make it.

Further reading

BEAGLEHOLE, J. C. *New Zealand: A Short History*, London, Allen & Unwin, 1936.

BEST, E. *The Maori*, Board of Maori Ethnological Research, Wellington, Whitcombe & Tombs, 1924, 2 vols.

BUTLER, S. *Erewhon*, London, 1882.

CAMPBELL, W. J. *Hydrotown: The Social History of an Industrial Boom Settlement*, University of Otago, 1957.

CLARK, A. H. *The Invasion of New Zealand by People, Plants and Animals*, New Brunswick, Rutgers Univ. Press, 1949.

CONDLIFFE, J. B. *New Zealand in the Making*, London, Allen & Unwin, 1929.

CUMBERLAND, K. B. 'Moas and men: New Zealand about A.D. 1250', *Geographical Review*, **52** (1962) 151–73.

CUMBERLAND, K. B. 'Aotearoa Maori: New Zealand about 1780', *Geographical Review*, **39** (1949) 401–24.

CUMBERLAND, K. B. 'A land despoiled: New Zealand about 1838', *New Zealand Geographer*, **6** (1950) 13–34.

CUMBERLAND, K. B. '"Jimmy Grants" and "Mihaneres": New Zealand about 1853', *Economic Geography*, **30** (1954) 70–89.

CUMBERLAND, K. B. 'A century's change: natural to cultural vegetation in New Zealand', *Geographical Review*, **31** (1941) 529–54.

CUMBERLAND, K. B. 'The agricultural regions of New Zealand', *Geographical Journal*, **112** (1948) 43–63.

CUMBERLAND, K. B. *Southwest Pacific: A Geography of Australia, New Zealand and their Pacific Island Neighbourhood*, 4th edn, Christchurch, Whitcombe & Tombs, 1967.

CUMBERLAND, K. B. *Soil Erosion in New Zealand: a geographic reconnaissance*, 2nd edn, Wellington, Whitcombe & Tombs, 1947.

CUMBERLAND, K. B. and FOX, J. W. *New Zealand: A Regional View*, 2nd edn, Christchurch, Whitcombe & Tombs, 1964.

CUMBERLAND, K. B. and HARGREAVES R. P. 'Middle Island Ascendant: New Zealand in 1881 (Part I)', *New Zealand Geographer*, **12** (1955) 95–118.

CUMBERLAND, K. B. and HARGREAVES, R. P. 'Middle Island Ascendant: New Zealand in 1881 (Part II)', *New Zealand Geographer*, **13** (1956) 51–74.

DIEFFENBACH, E. *Travels in New Zealand*, London, John Murray, 1843, 2 vols.

DUFF, R. S. *The Moa-hunter Period of Maori Culture*, Wellington, Department of Internal Affairs, 1950.

FARRELL, B. H. *Power in New Zealand*, Wellington, A. H. and A. W. Reed, 1961.

GARNIER, B. J. *The Climate of New Zealand. A Geographic Survey*, London, Arnold, 1958.

GUTHRIE-SMITH, H. *Tutira*, 2nd edn, London, Blackwoods, 1926.

HOCHSTETTER, F. VON. *New Zealand, its Physical Geography, Geology and Natural History*, Stuttgart, 1867.

LEVY, E. B. *Grasslands of New Zealand*, Wellington, 1955.

MCCASKILL, M., ed. *Land and Livelihood: Geographical Essays in Honour of George Jobberns*, Christchurch, New Zealand Geographical Society, Special Publication, 1962.

MCLINTOCK, A. H., ed. *A Descriptive Atlas of New Zealand*, Wellington, Government Printer, 1960.

MCLINTOCK, A. H., ed. *An Encyclopaedia of New Zealand*, Wellington, Government Printer, 1966, 3 vols.

METGE, JOAN. *The Maoris of New Zealand*, London, Routledge & Kegan Paul, 1967.

MULGAN, A. 'Literature and landscape in New Zealand', *New Zealand Geographer*, 2 (1946) 189–206.

New Zealand Official Year Book, Wellington, Government Printer (published annually).

SEARS, P. D. 'The regional variety of pasture growth in New Zealand', *New Zealand Geographer*, 1 (1945) 57–82.

SINCLAIR, K. *A History of New Zealand*, Harmondsworth, Penguin Books (Pelican), 1958.

SUTCH, W. B. *Colony or Nation?*, Sydney University Press, 1966.

SUTCH, W. B. *The Quest for Security in New Zealand, 1840 to 1966*, Wellington, Oxford University Press, 1966.

VAILE, E. *Pioneering the Pumice*, Auckland, Whitcombe & Tombs, 1940.

WARD, R. G. and WARD, MARION, eds. *New Zealand's Industrial Potential*, Auckland, New Zealand Geographical Society, 1960.

WATTERS, R. F., ed. *Land and Society in New Zealand: essays in historical geography*, Wellington, A. H. and A. W. Reed, 1965.

Index